A Guide to the

Flowering Plants and Ferns of Iceland

HÖRÐUR KRISTINSSON

A Guide to the
Flowering
Plants and Ferns
of Iceland

Mál og menning

Contents

Photographers

Björn Jónsson (1) 165 · Björn Rúriksson (1) 89 · Björn Þorsteinsson (1) 114 · Eyþór Einarsson (13) 35, 36, 44, 77, 86, 176, 184, 199, 228, 258, 285, 301, 338 (flower) · Guðfinna Karlsdóttir (2) 119, 262 · Helgi Hallgrímsson (19) 14, 27, 28, 31, 79 (fruit), 87, 92, 106, 117, 118 (fruit), 145, 152, 171, 187 (leaves), 213, 230,253, 338 (fruit), 361 · Jóhann Sigurbergsson (5) 60, 76 (fruit), 129, 174 (male), 257 · Oddur Sigurðsson (7) 81, 108, 112, 116 (flower), 227, 277, 356 · Ólafur Björn Guðmundsson (5) 15, 61, 168, 174 (female), 256 · Ólafur Jónsson (7) 120, 148 (fruit), 181, 196, 261, 269, 317 · Sigrún Helgadóttir (3) 69 (fruit), 195, 226 · Skúli Þór Magnússon (2) 41, 311 (fruit) · Snorri Baldursson (8) 18, 37, 58, 116 (fruit), 157, 194, 260, 268 · Sveinn Ólafsson (5) 21, 96, 248, 263, 359 · Þóra Ellen Þórhallsdóttir (1) 6. Other photographs, 302 in all, taken by Hörður Kristinsson.

A GUIDE TO THE FLOWERING PLANTS
AND FERNS OF ICELAND
Text: © 1986 Hörður Kristinsson.
Photographs: © Copyright see list above.
Design: Sigurþór Jakobsson.
Cover Design: Næst.
Drawings: Sigurður Valur Sigurðsson.
Maps: Sævar Pétursson.
Typesetting: Ljóshnit.
Coloranalysis and filmwork: Prentmyndastofan hf.
Printing and binding: Grafík hf.
First published by Örn og Örlygur 1987.
Second edition: Mál og menning, Reykjavík 1998.
Reprinted: Mál og menning, Reykjavík 2001.

Introduction

It was in early 1981 that I was approached by Örlygur Hálfdánarson of Örn og Örlygur Publishing House to discuss plans for an illustrated guide to Icelandic plants. The idea was to create a handbook where plants would be displayed in their natural habitats by means of colour plates. At that time I had already accumulated rather a large collection of photographs of Icelandic plants, taken over a period of over twenty years. It was decided that the first step should be to contact all plant photographers that we knew of, to select from among their collections the most suitable pictures for this book. The summers of 1982-1985 were used to take pictures of all species which had not been photographed before, and to take new ones to replace those photographs of my collection that did not fit very well into the framework of the book. Many grasses, sedges and aquatic plants had not been photographed before, and this was also the case for some extremely rare species as well as plants with very small flowers.

The result of this work is the first guide to include colour photographs of almost the whole of the Icelandic flora. It contains 382 illustrations of 365 species growing wild in Iceland. All other wild plants are treated in the text though not illustrated. Omitted plants fall into three categories: they are very rare, or they are foreign, unstable aliens, or they resemble other species in such a way that they can not be told apart by comparison with photographs. The many microspecies of hawkweeds and dandelions are also omitted. In all, 438 species are treated in the book.

This book is also the first to show the distribution of all species in Iceland by means of coloured maps. The maps are prepared from data collected for decades in many excursions by the author himself and many other professional and amateur botanists. Some of these data are published, others are obtained from herbaria or taken from file cards.

The *Guide to the Flowering Plants and Ferns of Iceland* is intended for all those who want to learn to know Icelandic wild plants in an easy way by looking up photographs rather than using keys. For those who require more detailed information or keys to every species, *Flóra Íslands* by Stefán Stefánsson (1947) can be recommended, or *Íslenzk ferðaflóra* by Áskell Löve (1970 and 1977). The former is available only in Icelandic, but the latter appeared in English in 1983 under the title *Flora of Iceland*.

The order of the plants in this book is not based on the relationship of the species, but rather on flower colours and other visible characteristics. This is done to make it easier for the untrained user to find plants in the book without expert knowledge of plant classification. A simple, illustrated key lists the characteristics by which the plants are ordered. By using the key the reader need only leaf through a few pages to find the plant he is looking for. This sequence has the disadvantage for experienced readers that related species, such as saxifrages, are located in different parts of the book because of their different colours.

Not all authorities agree on the number of wild flowering plants and ferns in Iceland. In the first place, it is a matter of opinion how many of the unstable foreign aliens should be regarded as Icelandic. In this book the main emphasis is on indigenous plants. All the more common aliens are included, but the rarest ones are omitted. In the second place, botanists do not always agree on how detailed the division into species should be. The separation of species in this guide does not go beyond what can be considered reasonable, so that the ordinary user should be able to identify all included species by their visible characteristics.

In some previous books, especially *Íslenzk Ferðaflóra* by Áskell Löve, the species are more narrowly defined than here, or further subdivided into subspecies and varieties. Many of these species are very difficult to distinguish, requiring microscopic investigation or even a chromosome count. I saw no reason to include all these species in this guide, especially since the value of such distinctions is disputable.

No plants are included in this guide whose occurrence in Iceland is not certain, and whose existence has not been verified in at least one locality in recent years. Some of the species included in Stefánsson's *Flóra Íslands*, third edition, and in *Íslenzk ferðaflóra* by Áskell Löve do not satisfy this requirement. Examples of such unverified species are *Scirpus setaceus* (Bristle Spikerush), *Myosotis ramosissima* (Early Forget-me-not), *Braya purpurascens*, *Pinguicula alpina* (Alpine Butterwort), *Eriophorum triste*, *Eriophorum russeolum*, *Euphrasia davidsonii*, *Euphrasia tenuis* and *Myriophyllum verticillatum* (Whorled Water-milfoil).

The English common names used in this book follow the second edition of the *English Names of Wild Flowers* compiled by J.G. Dony, S.L. Jury and F.H. Perring for the Botanical Society of the British Isles (B.S.B.I). This list of common names, however, includes only British plants. For northern species of flowering plants I have followed *The Wild Flowers of Britain and Northern Europe* by R. & A. Fitter. Hubbard's *Grasses*, and *British Sedges* by A.J. Jermy and T.G. Tutin were followed for names of grasses and sedges not included in the list of the (B.S.B.I). Many other commonly used names are included (in normal type) in the index with a reference to the correct plant number in the book, even where another name (boldface in the index) is used in the text.

The scientific names follow a checklist of Icelandic plants compiled by the Museum of Natural History in Reykjavík, which is, with few exceptions, based on *Flora Europaea*. They differ to some extent from the names used in *Flóra Íslands* by Stefán Stefánsson, which are largely out of date. All names used in that book, however, are included in the index. The scientific names used in the different editions of *Íslenzk ferðaflóra* and its English translation, *Flora of Iceland*, by Áskell Löve are not included in the index. The nomenclature in these works deviates so much from the traditional use of names, and varies so much from one edition to the next of that same book, that their inclusion would have made the index very bulky. It is recommended that users of Áskell Löve's floras make use of the Icelandic common names as a key to find the same species in this book.

Drawings in this book are all done by Sigurdur Valur Sigurdsson. They are drawn directly from plant parts, fresh or dried, or from photographs. Many of the smallest objects had to be drawn under a dissecting microscope. In spite of frequent difficulties in providing plant material of sufficient quality, the result surpassed all expectation and I am grateful to the artist for pleasant cooperation.

Sigurþór Jakobsson took care of the design and arranged the maps, drawings and photographs onto the pages with great taste. He also selected and trimmed the photographs in cooperation with the author. I thank him for a delightful and patient collaboration. I also thank the staff of Prentmyndastofan who prepared the colour photographs for printing, and the staff of Ljóshnit who set the text.

I am most grateful to Eyþór Einarsson, director of the herbarium of the Museum of Natural History in Reykjavík for giving me unlimited access to the herbarium and to other data in the Museum. This was very valuable, both for writing some of the plant descriptions, as well as for collecting data for the distribution maps. Eyþór Einarsson has also read the main part of the original Icelandic text, and made many suggestions for improvement. The English translation was read and corrected by Jón Skaptason.

I would like to thank Helgi Hallgrímsson for his permission to use the herbarium of the Akureyri Museum of Natural History, and Hjörleifur Guttormsson for the loan of unprinted data from the eastern districts of Iceland. I appreciate the loan of photographs from many plant photographers, whose names along with the photo numbers are listed on page 4. Finally, I am grateful for pleasant cooperation with the publisher, Örlygur Hálfdanarson, and the staff of Örn og Örlygur who helped to make this book what it is.

Reykjavík, May 1 1987,

Hörður Kristinsson

How to use this book

The easiest way to identify plants

The easiest way to identify plants using this book is to begin at the key on pp. 25-26.
The key divides all plants into groups A-H according to the colour of their flowers. When the correct colour group has been chosen, it is a simple matter to leaf through the corresponding plant numbers in the right-hand column. If your specimen, for instance, has blue flowers it belongs to group A, and should therefore be among the first 24 flowers in the book.
The plants in groups E, F and H are further divided into categories according to the size and shape of their flowers. If your plant belongs to one of these groups, you should use the text and illustrations of the key to arrive at the correct plant numbers in the right-hand column, and then look through the corresponding photographs in the book. In the H-class, which includes aquatic plants, ferns, grasses and sedges, the numbered classes are further subdivided according to other characteristics such as the size and shape of the leaves. Here again, the illustrations and the text will direct you to a limited number of photographs which you can compare to your specimen.
Having found the photograph that best fits your plant, it is important to read through the description and check the characteristics pointed out in the text and illustrated in the margins. Should there be any doubt about the identification after this comparison, you should check the possibility of confusion with other similar species pointed out under the heading **Sim:** in the plant description. This should in most cases lead to a correct identification. If this still leads you to the wrong photograph, you should try looking at the few additional species given for some of the key groups on p. 27 immediately following the key. For example, if you traced your plant to group H6, and you did not find it among plants number 264-272, a quick look at p. 27 will direct you to the additional numbers 137, 213, and 215. Finally, if all this fails, please check if one of the reasons given in the next chapter might explain your problem.

For consideration if identification fails

1.   Among all plants with red, pink, violet, or blue flowers, you will occasionally find individuals with white flowers. Such plants, often several individuals in a group, could lead you astray if you try to identify them as white-flowered plants.
2.   Among most plants that as a rule have a fixed number of petals on each flower, e.g. five, you will occasionally come across individuals or single flowers with a different number of petals, e.g. four or six. In order to avoid misidentification for this reason, you should always examine several flowers, and base your identification on the dominating petal number rather than on a single flower.
3.   Be careful when you identify violet, pink or red flower colours. These colours are evaluated differently by different people, and though the key takes this into account by overlapping colour groups, it is a good idea to check other related colours if the first choice fails.
4.   Most plants show considerable variation in growth forms at their various stages of development from embryo to maturity. In a single photograph it is usually possible to show only one of these stages. If the plant you are identifying is at a different stage of development than the photograph depicts, it may be very difficult to recognize. Here, the drawings in the margins will help in some cases by showing a part of the plant, e.g. the fruit, at a different stage.
5.   If the plant you want to identify was found growing near an abandoned garden or farm or in an industrial area, it may well be an alien that has escaped from cultivation, or it may have been introduced accidentally with grass-seed or in some other way by a human agent. In such cases, the species may not be included in this book, and identification will fail for that reason. This book

is intended primarily for use in identifying native Icelandic species, even though all common aliens are included.

6. To verify some of the characteristics mentioned in the descriptions, e.g. hairs or parts of small flowers, a good magnifier may be necessary. Without one you run the risk of overlooking important identifying factors. Suitable magnifying glasses for plant identification are quite small (2 cm or less in diameter), but they magnify 8-12 times.

7. Some plants, especially in the H-group which includes all grasses, rushes and sedges, are difficult to identify by the colour photos alone. Those who lack the necessary experience, time or patience will probably have to resign themselves to not being able to identify all these species. Others are referred to more detailed identification books with keys to all Icelandic species. At present, only one such book, *The Flora of Iceland* by Áskell Löve, is available in English.

Sequence of plant species

In this book, plants are ordered by the colour of their flowers and by other simple, pronounced characteristics, rather than by relationship. The same characteristics are used in the key on page 25. The book starts with blue flowers, going gradually through violet to red. The red flowers are followed by light red, pink and finally white flowers. Following the white flowers are yellow flowers, and then green. The rest of the species, with other or indefinitive flower colours are ordered according to type of foliage leaves. The last group consists of plants with grass-like leaves, but since these are quite numerous, the grass-like plants are ordered by type of inflorescence.

This order was chosen to make the book easier to use for those without expert knowledge of plants. As a result, related plants, even within the same genus, may be spread throughout the book if their flowers are of different colours. For example, the Rose family is found scattered throughout the book according to the colour and size of its members' flowers. No doubt some users with experience of plants will find this a bit irritating, but on p. 290 all the families represented in the book are listed with references to plant numbers, and this should help to locate all the plants in the book belonging to any given family.

Photographs

The photographs usually show the plants in flower. Some plant species are represented by two photographs, usually of flower and fruit or of female and male individuals of the same, unisexual species. The photographs were usually selected with a view to showing as many characteristics of the plant as possible, both the flowers and the leaves. All are printed from colour slides, usually taken on Kodak or Agfa film in the period 1962-1985. A few have been published previously as part of a slide collection for the State Educational Film Library. A list of photographers can be found on page 4.

Drawings

The marginal drawings usually show single plant parts to illustrate important identifying characteristics better than is possible in a single photograph. They often represent a different stage of development than the photograph. Drawings of grasses and sedges usually show spikelets or utricles. Some of them are useful only if a magnifier is available. Following every drawing is the magnification (m) or reduction (r) factor in parentheses.

The drawings are based variously on fresh plants, dried herbarium specimens, or close-up photographs. In a few cases other published drawings were used as a source. All drawings in the book are by Sigurdur Valur Sigurdsson.

Plant descriptions

Descriptions of plant species usually begin with the flowers. Then the leaves and stems are described. Exceptions are plants that rarely flower, or have very small and inconspicuous flowers. In such cases, other parts are described before the flowers.

Descriptions of colour, both in the key and in the text, can be very difficult. Judgement of colours is often very personal, and the terms used may be interpreted in different ways by different individuals. White, for example, is used in rather a wide sense in this book. Besides pure white, it includes creamy white, dull white, and even white with a faint yellowish or grayish green tint. By using white in this sense, the limits between white and yellow are kept sharper than otherwise would be possible. Colours representing a mixture of blue and red are called violet or purple. There is no sharp division between blue, violet or red in flower colours. Pink is used for colours formed by the addition of a slight shade of red to white. If there is any hint of blue besides the red in the white colour, it is classified as light violet rather than pink. There is, however, no clear distinction between pink and light violet flowers, and this should be kept in mind by the users of the book.

The size of plant parts is given as an average of the most common sizes. The measurements are by no means intended to cover the total variation a plant may express under different growth conditions. The same must be kept in mind when the number of petals, sepals, stamens and pistils is determined. The given numbers should be regarded as the most frequent ones, but single flowers or individuals may occasionally deviate from these.

When the term "leaves" is used without further qualification, foliage leaves are always meant and not flower leaves.

Whenever possible, the descriptions were made directly from the observation of living plants. Dried herbarium specimens were also often used to verify the described characteristics. In nearly all cases, however, the descriptions are based on Icelandic specimens; only in a very few cases are descriptions based on the text of other books.

At the end of the actual descriptions of the plants, you will find additional information under the abbreviated headings **H:** for the height of the plant, **Hab:** for its habitat, **Sim:** for remarks on similar species, which might cause confusion, **Fl:** for the main flowering time, and **I:** for its common name in Icelandic.

Under **H:** (height of the plant) the same principle is followed as for measurements of plant parts. The figure is selected to give the usual height of the plant from the ground, ignoring the smallest and tallest individuals, which may well deviate from the given limits.

Under **Hab:** (habitat) the type of vegetation, landscape or other environmental conditions in which the plant is most commonly found is given. This information is based on the author's experience. It is also noted how common or rare the plant is within its habitat and within the area shown on the distribution maps. This is indicated by labels such as very common, common, widespread, rather widespread, rather rare, rare and very rare, according to the author's evaluation.

Under **Sim:** (similar species) those plants are mentioned, which are most likely to cause confusion when the plant is identified with reference to the text or photograph. The figures in parentheses following the plant name refer to the plant's number in the book, so that they may be looked up and compared. The characteristics most useful in distinguishing the species are also pointed out.

Under **Fl:** (flowering) the usual flowering time is indicated by months. Usually this is the same time as given in *Flóra Íslands* by Stefán Stefánsson, but in a few cases this time has been changed based on more recent information. Many species begin flowering in late May or early June, and in such cases the flowering time May-June may be given, even though the plants usually begin flowering near the end of May. In general, the lowland flowering time is given, except in the case of those plants which are restricted to high altitudes. Consequently, a later flowering time may be expected for plants in the northernmost outposts or in the mountains than indicated in the text.

Under **I:** the most frequent Icelandic common name for the plant is given.

Immediately following some of the plant descriptions there may be a short description of an additional species, usually rare and therefore not pictured in the book. Such species are located under the number of the most related or similar species. These secondary descriptions are headed by the number of the pictured species followed by the letter A (or B if there are two additional species under the same number).

Distribution maps

The distribution maps show in red the areas of the country where the plant in question has been found. Usually it is very unlikely for the species to be found outside this area, i.e. where native Icelandic plants are concerned. Should this occur, however, it would be appreciated if users of this book would report such new discoveries to one of the Museums of Natural History in Iceland so that the maps may be updated for future editions.

On the other hand, in the case of imported, foreign species or aliens, there are likely to be gaps in the distribution maps, due to insufficient information. Many of the alien plants move around; they die out in one locality and reappear in new ones. Some of them have been steadily widening their distribution in the last years, and may already be present in many unrecorded localities. Cow Parsley, Caraway, Creeping Thistle and White Dead-nettle are examples of such species, which are probably present in many more localities than the maps indicate.

It should be noted that some plants may be scattered or even rare within areas marked red. Continuous colour in the map may represent only a few, single localities too close together for separation on such a small-scale map.

Where such localities are far enough apart, they are marked as dots. In some cases such a dot may represent a single, small spot where the species has been observed.

In the preparation of the maps, all available data have been used, published and unpublished. Great quantities of filed data are stored in the Museums of Natural History in Reykjavík, Akureyri and Neskaupstaður. These data have been collected by many botanists and volunteers who use the Icelandic national grid system as a basis for their data collection. The first computer-printed maps based on the grid system were used for comparison when drawing the distribution maps. In areas for which few data were available, the distributional limits were estimated according to the best available information. Known altitudinal limits of the species in Iceland and climatical factors were taken into account when marking areas with insufficient data.

It is not possible here to mention all the many botanists, collectors, and amateurs, who have contributed data for the distribution maps, but this will be remedied in due course when the computerized distribution maps are published.

Glossary of botanical terms

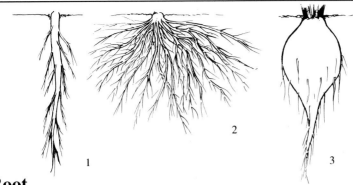

Root

The basic parts of every plant are root, stem and leaves. The primary root emerging from the germinating seed is called a **radicle** (9c). If the radicle grows and develops into the main root of the plant, it is known as a **taproot** (1). If it stops growing soon after germination, and many lateral roots function throughout the plant's life, the plant is said to have **fibrous roots** (2). The main root may swell into a very thick, turnip-like food storage organ (3), or the lateral roots may swell and form **tuberous roots**.

Stem

The underground part of the stem is called a **rhizome**. It can be erect (**rootstock**) or horizontal just below the ground surface. The aerial stem can also be either **erect** (4), **ascending** (5) or **prostrate** (6). If roots grow out from the nodes of a horizontal (creeping) stem, it is said to be **rooting** (6). Long side-branches that grow horizontally out from the base or from the rhizome, are called **stolons** (7) if they are underground, and **runners** if they are above the ground. They are often **rooting** at the nodes. The stems of grasses and sedges are often called **culms**.

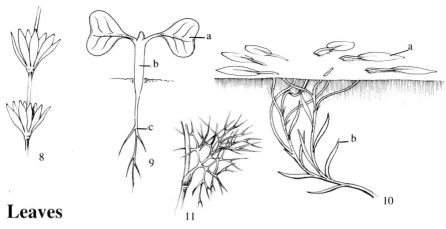

Leaves

A shoot is a stem or part of a stem with leaves. Leaves are of different types. The first leaves appearing from a germinating seed are the **cotyledons** (9a). The part of the stem below the cotyledons, is called a **hypocotyl** (9b). **Foliage leaves** are the largest green leaves of the above-ground stem. Small **scale leaves** (7a) sometimes grow near the base of the stem or on the underground part of the stem. They are often membranous. Small leaves above the foliage leaves, usually in the inflorescence or on flowering branches, are called **bracts** (4a). The leaves that protect the apical or axillary buds are called **bud scales** (57a).

Aquatic plants may have both **floating leaves** (10a) and **submerged leaves** (10b), which often differ in shape. The submerged leaves are often divided into filiform segments (11).

Position of leaves

Leaves are attached to the stem at the **nodes** (12e). If only a single leaf is present on each node, the leaves are called **alternate** (5). They are **opposite**, when two leaves are on each node (6), and **decussate** if each pair of opposite leaves forms a right angle with the nearest lower and upper pairs of leaves. The leaves can also be in **whorls** (8) if three or more leaves are on each node. The part of the stem between two nodes is called an **internode**. Long internodes result in a sparsely leaved stem, but dense-leaved stems have short internodes. If the internodes remain compressed without elongating, the leaves form a **rosette**, usually a basal rosette (4b). Basal leaves are sometimes called **radical leaves** to distinguish them from **stem leaves** or **culm leaves**.

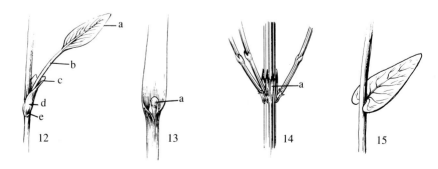

Foliage leaves

The foliage leaf is the main organ of photosynthesis. It consists of three parts: **blade** (12a), **petiole** or **leaf stalk** (12b), and **leaf base** (12d). The base may form a **sheath** (12) around the stem. Small leaves, called **stipules**, sometimes grow where the leaf base and petiole meet (12c). Stalkless leaves are called **sessile**; if the base of the blade is grown halfway around the stem, they are said to be **clasping** (15). Grass leaves have a small, erect membrane at the base, the **ligule** (13a).

Horsetails have stem-sheaths on every node (14a), terminating in a whorl of teeth.

Veins of leaves

A bundle of veins leads from the stem through the petiole into the blade where it forms different types of branching patterns. The main bundle, if it continues straight through the center of the leaf, is called a **midrib**. If it forms many lateral veins on both sides, the leaf is **pinnate-veined** (23-26). If the main bundle divides into many, nearly equal veins immediately at the base of the leaf, it is called **palmate-veined** (31). Leaves that have many similar veins running parallel from the base to the tip, are **parallel-veined** (17). These veins may either be straight, as in grasses (17), or curved (27). If the stalk is attached directly to the centre of the lower leaf surface, and not to the margin, with the veins radiating in a star-like pattern from the centre, the leaf is **stellate-veined**.

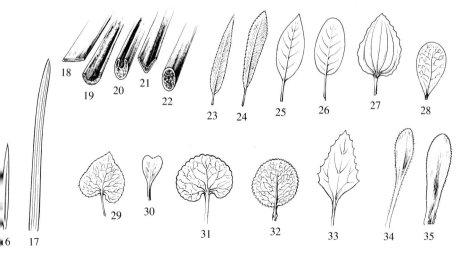

Leaf shape

Leaves have a great variety of shapes. **Needle-shaped** leaves are narrow and stiff, with sharp points (16). **Linear** leaves are also narrow with straight, parallel sides (17). Linear leaves are often **flat** in section (18). But if their margin is curved upwards (**incurved** or **involute**) and the leaf therefore U-shaped in section the leaves are said to be **channelled** (19, 20). If their section is V-shaped, they are **keeled** (21), and those which are round in section are called **filiform** or thread-shaped (22).

Lanceolate leaves (23) are oblong, their length being three or more times their width, and pointed at both ends. The sides are curved and the blade of the leaf is broadest at or just below the middle. If the broadest part is above the centre, the leaf is **oblanceolate** (24). **Elliptic** leaves (25, 26) are broader, about twice as long as they are broad, broadest around the middle, the ends either pointed (25) or rounded (26). **Ovate** leaves are similar in shape, but broader below the middle (27), and **obovate** leaves are broadest above the middle (28). **Cordate** leaves are heart-shaped (29) with a pointed tip and the stalk attached in the notch. If the stalk is attached to the pointed end, the leaf is **obcordate** (30). **Reniform** (or kidney-shaped) leaves (31) have a similar shape, but with a rounded tip and no point. **Round** leaves (32) are almost circular in outline. **Rhomboid** leaves (33) are shaped like slightly distorted diamonds. **Spatulate** leaves (34) are narrow at the base, broadening like a spoon with a rounded end. **Ligulate** leaves (35) have a narrow base, tapering gradually towards the round or slightly pointed tip.

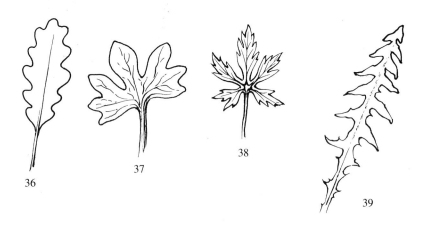

36
37
38
39

Leaf margins

Leaves with smooth, straight margins are called **entire** (25, 26). If notches or slits are cut into the margin, the leaf is **incised**. If the inscisions are small, the leaf is **dentate** or **toothed** (23, 24), but if they are deeper the leaf is **lobed** (36, 37) or **dissected** (38, 39). The leaf parts in between the incisions are called **teeth** or **lobes** depending on the depth of the incisions. The teeth can be sharp and oblique like on a saw, and the leaves are then **serrate** (24), or they may be curved on **crenate** leaves (31). If the leaves are so deeply dissected that the incisions reach the midrib or the base, the leaf is called **palmatifid** (38) or **pinnatifid** (39) according to the venation. If the leaf margin is transparent, like a thin membrane, the leaf has a **membranous margin**.

Leaf tips

The tips of leaves and other plant parts can vary greatly in shape. If the margins of both sides meet
to form a point, the leaves are **pointed** or **acute** (40). Tips with curved, round outlines are said
to be **obtuse** or **blunt** (41). If a blunt leaf-tip terminates in a very small, sharp point, the leaf is
mucronate (42). If the tip of a leaf looks like it has been cut straight across, the leaf is said to be
truncate (43). If the end has a shallow, curved notch it is **retuse** (44), but if a sharp notch is cut
into the end, the tip is **emarginate** or **notched** (45).

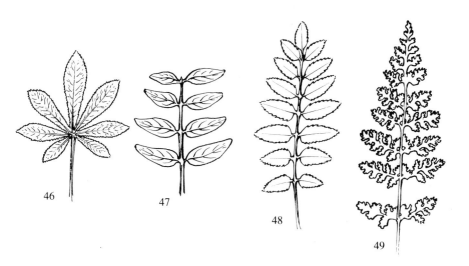

Compound leaves

Leaves that are divided into separate units are called **compound leaves** (46-49). The single leaf
parts are called **leaflets**. If all the leaflets rise from the same point, and the compound leaf is consequently palmate-veined, the leaf is called **palmate** (46). If the leaflets grow in rows out from
both sides of the midrib, the leaf is called **pinnate** (47, 48). An **even-pinnate** leaf (47) has an e-
qual number of leaflets on each side, without a terminal leaflet. An **odd-pinnate** leaf (48) has one
terminal leaflet apart from the lateral leaflets. If the leaflets of a pinnate leaf are themselves pinnate, the leaf is called **bipinnate** (49). The pinnate leaflets are then distinguished as **primary leaf-
lets** from their own leaflets which are secondary leaflets. **Secondary leaflets**, which are again
pinnate form **tertiary leaflets**, and the compound leaf is then called **tripinnate**. If only the lower
part of a blade is pinnate (as on a fern), and the upper part is pinnatifid rather than pinnate, the
leaf is said to be **semi-pinnate**.

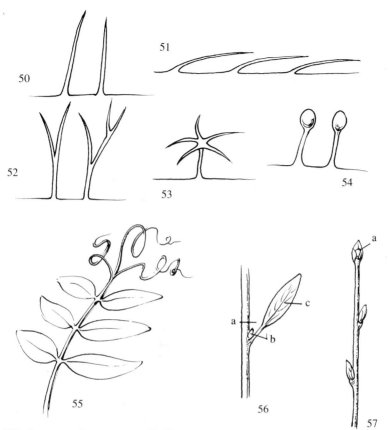

Hairs, spines, tendrils.

Plants, or parts of plants, are often covered with hairs. These hairs are usually **simple** (unbranched) (50, 51) and can be either **erect** (outstanding) (50), or **appressed** (51). Appressed hairs lie parallel and close to the surface of the plant. Occasionally, hairs are branched. They are then called **forked hairs** (52) or **stellate hairs** (53) according to the pattern of branching. Many hairs have a small, knob-like head on the tip. These are called **glandular hairs** or **glands** (54). Glandular hairs usually secrete a liquid, often strong-smelling and/or sticky. Leaves with hairs along the margin are called **ciliate** (34). Some plant parts, e.g. leaflets of compound leaves, can be transformed into **tendrils** (55), which coil around stems or petioles of neighbour-plants for support. Some plants have hard **spines** or **bristles**. These can be formed from teeth of leaves, stipules, hairs, or lateral branches.

Lateral stems

Side branches always grow from lateral **buds** (56b) located in the **leaf axils**, the upper angle between the leaf and the stem. The leaf is then called the **bract** (56c) of the lateral branch or flower growing out of the bud. The bract can either be a large foliage leaf, or a very incomplete, small, membranous scale on the inflorescence. The buds are known as **axillary buds** or **terminal buds** depending on their location. Buds that survive the winter above ground are protected by scaly, thick leaves called **bud scales** (57).

16

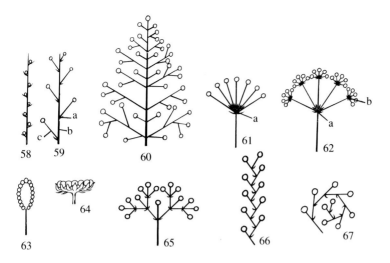

58   59   60   61   62   63   64   65   66   67

Inflorescences

Flowers are usually located in the upper part of a plant, either single, on top of the stem or in the upper leaf axils, or several, combined into so-called **inflorescences**. Inflorescences are classified according to their branching pattern. The flowers usually grow each from an axillary bud subtended by a **bract** (59a). The main stem supporting the bracts and the flowers is called the **inflorescence axis** (59b). Each individual flower can be on a short or long stalk called a **pedicel** (59c), or it can be sessile. The pedicel sometimes has one or two tiny leaves also called bracts. If the inflorescence axis is extended, and the flowers unstalked, we have an inflorescence called a **spike** (58), but if each of the flowers is borne on a long pedicel, we have a **raceme** (59). Spikes and racemes can grow terminally and form new flowers as long as growth conditions are present. They are for this reason sometimes known as open inflorescences. **Catkins** are spike-like, unisexual inflorescences on birches and willows, which generally fall off the plant in one piece. **Panicles** (60) are common inflorescences on many grasses. They resemble compound racemes, which have a limited growth, and are therefore known as closed inflorescences. If the inflorescence axis is short and stout, and the flowers are on long pedicels, we have an **umbel** (61). The bracts of all the flowers in an umbel form a whorl at the base called an **involucrum** (61a). If the branches of an umbel bear new secondary umbels at the tip instead of single flowers, we have a **compound umbel** with several **umbellules** (62). The bracts of the secondary umbels form a whorl at the base called an **involucrellum**. If the flowers are unstalked, growing out from a compact, round, ovate or flat inflorescence axis, we have an inflorescence called a **head** (63-64). At the base or on the outside of the head there are usually many protecting leaves called **involucral bracts**. A common feature of all the inflorescences mentioned so far is that the central or terminal flowers are the last to open. Such inflorescences are said to be **racemose**. **Cymose** inflorescences start flowering in the centre, and the marginal flowers are the last to open. A **dichasium** (dichasial cyme) is a cymose inflorescence (65). It forms the first flower terminally on a stem. Two side branches grow out from the next bracts below the terminal flower, and these side branches both form a single flower at the tip. Two side branches then grow from the axils of the bracts of each of the two primary branches, and all four produce a terminal flower and so on. If such an inflorescence produces only a single lateral flower branch each time instead of two (on plants having alternate leaves instead of opposite), it is called **monochasium** or monchasial cyme (66, 67).

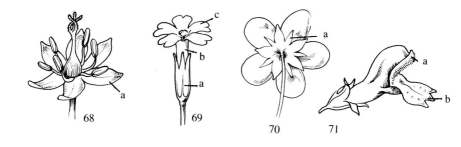

Flowers and perianth

The terminal, often disc-like part of the stem bearing the leaves of the flower is called a **receptacle** (78a-80a).

The flower leaves are of four types: **Sepals** (78b) are the lowest or marginal leaves, together forming a whorl called a **calyx**; above them are the **petals**, which combined form a whorl called a **corolla** (78c). Next are the **stamens** (78d), and finally the **carpels** which are often fused together to form the **pistil** (78e) in the centre of the flower. The sepals are usually green, but the petals and stamens are usually bright-coloured. Together, the sepals and petals form the **perianth** of the flower, but in flowers with no distinction between sepals and petals, the terms perianth and **perianth leaves** (68a) are used instead. Perianth leaves are usually also in a whorl on the receptacle. The flowers are called three-parted, four-parted, five-parted etc. depending on the number of sepals or petals in the perianth. If all the sepals are fused, the calyx is called **gamosepalous** (69), but if the sepals are individually free, the calyx is **polysepalous** (78). Corresponding terms, **gamopetalous** (69, 71) and **polypetalous** (70), are used for the corolla. When small, regular appendages are formed between the sepals as in the Rose family, they are known together as an **epicalyx** (70a). A gamopetalous corolla often forms a **tube** (69b) in the lower part, but the petal tips are usually free like the petal lobes. If the petal lobes expand horizontally out from the tube, they form a **collar** (69c). The often narrow opening of the tube is called a **throat**. Wart-like protuberances sometimes grow out from the throat. If all the petals are of equal size and shape with regular intervals, the flower is called **regular** (69,70) but otherwise irregular (71). Regular flowers are **radially symmetric** (68-70), i.e. they can be divided radially into equal segments. **Bilateral** flowers can be divided along two planes into equal parts. **Irregular** flowers can usually be divided along one plane into two equal parts, and are then called **zygomorphic** (71). A corolla (or calyx) is **bilabiate**, if the petals (sepals) are divided into two groups, one pointing downwards and the other upwards, forming a **lower lip** (71b) and **upper lip** (71a). The flowers of violets, butterworts and orchids form a small sac down from the perianth, known as a **spur**.

Stamens

The stamens bear **anthers** (72a) at the tip, borne by a stalk called a **filament** (72b). The anthers usually contain two **pollen sacs**, which produce the **pollen grains**. Flowers which bear only stamens (**male flowers**) or pistils (**female flower**) but not both, are called **unisexual**, but flowers which contain both are called **bisexual** (68, 78). Male flowers and female flowers are often combined on the same plant (**monoecious** plant) which is then bisexual itself even though the single flowers are unisexual. Male and female flowers can also be separate on different individuals (**dioecious** plant) which means that the plant is unisexual like the flowers.

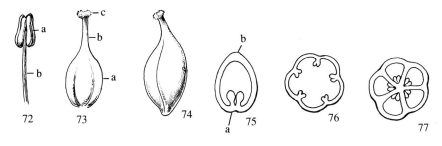

Pistils

The **pistil** (73) is shaped like a bottle, hollow inside or filled with juicy tissue. The lowest and widest part of the pistil is called an **ovary** (73a). It terminates in a narrow **style**, like the neck of a bottle (73b), and is tipped with the **stigma** (73c). The function of the stigma is to receive the **pollen** grains, and it is therefore usually haired and sticky, either knob-shaped or divided into two or more branches. The pistil is made up of one or more leaves called **carpels**. If a single carpel makes up the pistil (74), both edges are curved to the same side until they meet and fuse to form the **ventral suture** (75a). The midrib of the carpel forms the **dorsal suture** (75b). If the pistil is made up of several carpels, they are usually arranged side by side to form a circle, with the margins grown together (73, 76). If the carpels together form a large locule inside the pistil, it is said to be **unilocular** (76). The margin of the carpels can also extend towards the centre of the pistil, whereby each carpel forms separate a locule, and the pistil is then said to be **plurilocular** (77).

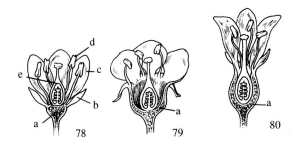

Position of flower parts

Depending on the position of the perianth and stamens in relation to the pistil, flowers can be **hypogynous, perigynous** or **epigynous**. Most flowers are **hypogynous** (78), i.e. the perianth and the stamens are located below or around the pistil. **Perigynous** (79) flowers have a receptacle shaped like a bowl, with the pistil free on the bottom and the perianth and stamens located on the edges of the bowl all around. **Epigynous** (80) flowers, have the pistil sunk into the receptacle, which is elevated and grows all around the pistil and united with it all the way up. The perianth leaves and stamens are then located on the margin of the receptacle at the tip of the pistil. Mature fruits betray their origin in hypogynous or epigynous flowers by the position of the calyx leaves which are found either sitting around the fruit stalk (as on tomatoes), or opposite at the top of the fruit (as on apples).

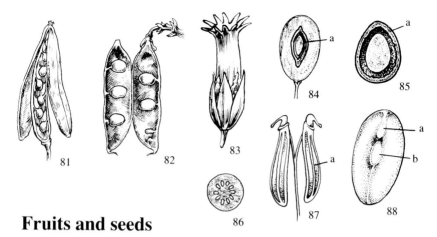

Fruits and seeds

The pistil develops into **fruits**, containing one or more **seeds** at maturity. The seeds are protected by a **seed coat**, which is usually of a dark colour. Visible on the outside of the seed is the radicle (88a) which develops into a root when the seed germinates. Inside the seed are the **cotyledons** (9a), the first leaves that appear at germination. The chord that connects the immature seed, the **ovule**, to the **placenta**, is called a **funiculus**, and the place of attachment remains visible as a scar on the seed, called a **hylum** (88b).

Fruits are of many different types. Fruits that dry and open at maturity are **dehiscent**, usually taking the form of **capsules** (81-83). They can be made up of single or many carpels, and open in different ways. A **silique** (81) is a capsule made of two carpels, and divided into two compartments by a transparent membrane. Siliques are characteristic of the Mustard family. A short silique, less than three times longer than wide, is called a **silicle. Pods** are made of a single carpel (82), which opens both at the dorsal and ventral suture. A third type of capsule is found in the Pink family, made up of many carpels, opening at the juncture of the carpels, and sometimes also along their midrib (83), thus forming the same or double the number of marginal teeth as the carpels. Many fruits, especially those which are juicy and fleshy, do not open at maturity (**indehiscent** fruits). Such a fruit is called a **drupe** (84) if the innermost layer forms a stone around the seed, but a **berry** (86) if the seeds are protected only by the seed coat. Drupes usually contain only one seed, and berries many, but there are some exceptions. If the whole fruit wall is hard and dry like a stone, the fruit is called a **nut** (85). Some types of nuts have the fruit wall grown to the seed coat, like the **achene** of dandelions and hawkweeds. A **schizocarp** is a fruit with more than one seed, and the seed coat grown to the fruit wall. The schizocarp splits at maturity into several pieces, called **merocarps** (87a), each containing one seed and section of the fruit.

Lifespan and habitat

An **annual** is a plant that completes its total life cycle within a single year. The seeds of some annuals germinate in the fall, but those of others in the spring. **Biennial** plants usually form a leaf rosette and store reserve food in the first summer, then flower and mature their seeds in the second year before they die. Some of them need to accumulate reserves for several years before they flower. **Perennial** plants live many years, generally flowering and producing seeds every year.

The characteristic environment a given plant species selects to grow in, a place with the special requirements that the plant needs to thrive, is known as a **habitat**. Some of the Icelandic habitats differ from those most commonly found in Middle or Western Europe. **Heath** or **heathland** is

20

used for terrain covered with small **hummocks** (Icel. "þúfur") and, generally, a growth of dwarf-shrubs. **Snowbeds** are hollows or depressions in the landscape which are filled with snow during the winter and late into spring. The snow provides important protection for some plants through winter and spring. Lava fields and volcanic deserts are another example of typical habitats in Iceland. Foreign, introduced plants are often unstable colonizers, growing for only one or a few years in a certain place, then disappearing and occasionally appearing in another place. Such a species is called an **unstable alien**. If an alien plant settles permanently in a given place, it is called a **naturalized alien**.

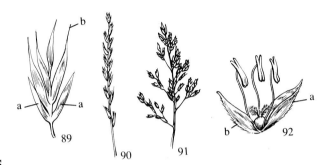

Grasses

The flowers of grasses differ from the flowers of dicotyledones. They are usually borne in compound inflorescences. The flowers are single or several in very small, compact inflorescences called **spikelets** (89). Many spikelets are arranged into a **compound spike** (90) or **panicle** (91). In the panicle, the spikelets are on short or long stalks, often branched. In a compound spike the spikelets are sessile on the inflorescence axis. The two small leaves at the base of the spikelet are called the **upper** and **lower glumes** (89a). The flowers themselves also bear two small leaves instead of a perianth, the upper one called a **palea** and the lower one a **lemma** (92a,b). A very fine bristle which sometimes grows out from the glumes or the lemma, is called an **awn** (89b). The awn may be quite long, even exceeding the spikelet itself in length. Veins are sometimes visible as raised **nerves** on the glumes or the lemma. The glumes or the lemma may occasionally develop into small leaves if the panicle is **viviparous**. The stem of the grasses is usually called a **culm**.

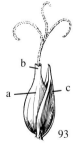

Sedges

The pistil of sedges is surrounded by a bottle-shaped container called an **utricle** (93a). Its style grows out through a narrow opening at its tip, which is sometimes extended to form a **beak** (93b). **Nerves** (veins) may be visible from the outside. Sedge flowers have no perianth, but one bract is located at the front of each flower in the spikes, usually called a **scale** (93c). Occasionally, the scale more or less covers the utricle.

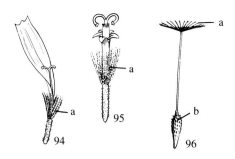

Flowerheads

The **flowerheads** of the Daisy family are very compact and look like single flowers, but they consist in reality of numerous small flowers called **florets** (94, 95). The florets are sometimes of two different types in the same head. The white marginal flowers, or **rayflorets**, of the Sea Mayweed have a **ligulate** corolla (94), which means that the petals are fused at the sides forming a sideways-curved tongue. The yellow flowers in the centre, the **discflorets**, have a **tubular** corolla (95). The sepals of these florets form a small whorl of hairs (94a, 95a) around the top of the pistil. When the fruit matures, these hairs become a **pappus** (96a) which helps in the dissemination of the fruit.

Legumes

The flowers of the Pea family have a characteristic shape. The uppermost petal, called a **banner** (97a), is very large. Two narrower leaves, one on each side, are called **wings** (97b). Underneath are two petals fused into a **keel** (97c) enclosing the stamens.

Ferns, horsetails and clubmosses

Ferns neither flower nor produce seeds. Instead, they have small, usually brown, raised spots on the underside of their leaves called **sori** (98) . The sori are in reality clusters of many small, stalked **sporangia** (99a). A small, membranous flap is often seen on top of the sorus, or at its side, called an **indusium** (99b). Stems or leaves that carry sporangia are said to be **fertile**, those without are **sterile**. Horsetails and clubmosses carry sporangia in sporangial cones or **strobilus** at the apex of fertile stems.

Index to Glossary

Key

An asterix at the end of a line refers to additional species on page 27.

A Flowers blue 1–24*

B Flowers violet 21–39*

C Flowers red 34–60*

D Flowers pink 53–73*

E Flowers white

    1 Flowers large, more than 1 cm wide, or many together in compact heads 70–95*

    2 Flowers small, less than 1 cm wide, 5-parted, with free petals, neither in umbel nor head 89–116*

    3 Flowers small, crowded in umbellate inflorescences 117–126

    4 Flowers small, 4-parted (or 3-parted), with free petals 127–146*

    5 Flowers small, petals connected 143–155*

F Flowers yellow

    1 Flowers large, more than 1 cm wide, not in heads 156–168

    2 Flowers small, less than 1 cm wide, 5-parted, petals free. 166–169

    3 Flowers small, 4-parted (or 3-parted), with free petals 170–176

    4 Flowers small, not in heads, petals connected . 176–181*

    5 Flowers crowded in compact heads 182–189

G Flowers green or yellowish green, not flushed with red. 188–196*

25

H Flowers with other colours, often varicoloured (reddish or green, tawny, brown, greyish) or flowers absent

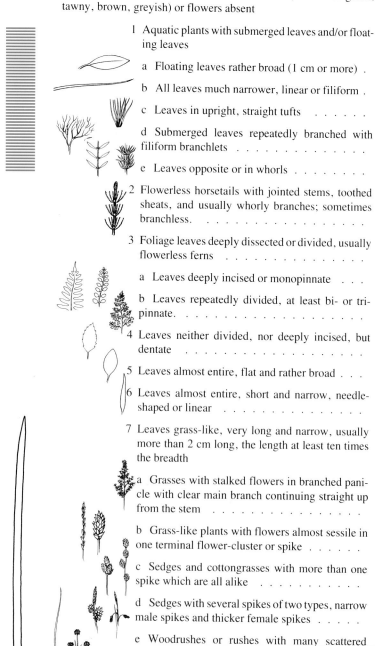

1 Aquatic plants with submerged leaves and/or floating leaves

   a Floating leaves rather broad (1 cm or more) . 197–201

   b All leaves much narrower, linear or filiform . 202–208*

   c Leaves in upright, straight tufts 209–210*

   d Submerged leaves repeatedly branched with filiform branchlets 211–212*

   e Leaves opposite or in whorls 213–217

2 Flowerless horsetails with jointed stems, toothed sheats, and usually whorly branches; sometimes branchless. 217–223

3 Foliage leaves deeply dissected or divided, usually flowerless ferns

   a Leaves deeply incised or monopinnate . . . 224–232

   b Leaves repeatedly divided, at least bi- or tripinnate. 232–239*

4 Leaves neither divided, nor deeply incised, but dentate 240–243*

5 Leaves almost entire, flat and rather broad . . . 244–266*

6 Leaves almost entire, short and narrow, needle-shaped or linear 264–272*

7 Leaves grass-like, very long and narrow, usually more than 2 cm long, the length at least ten times the breadth

   a Grasses with stalked flowers in branched panicle with clear main branch continuing straight up from the stem 273–298

   b Grass-like plants with flowers almost sessile in one terminal flower-cluster or spike 296–329*

   c Sedges and cottongrasses with more than one spike which are all alike 325–339

   d Sedges with several spikes of two types, narrow male spikes and thicker female spikes 339–354*

   e Woodrushes or rushes with many scattered flower clusters, or with one to several lateral flower-clusters 355–365*

Species that could belong to more than one key group.

A   Blue Moor-grass 298, Mat-grass 308.

B   Lady Smock 62, Common Mudwort 64, Glacier Buttercup 70, Alpine Fleabane 73, Sea Rocket 128, Arctic Eyebright 153A, Upright Lousewort 179, Yellow-rattle 180, Marsh Arrow-grass 309.

C   Field Scabious 17A, Bilberry 68, Bog Bilberry 69, Mare's-tail 216, Common Sorrel 253, Sheep's Sorrel 254, Mountain Sorrel 256, Frog Orchid 257, Crow-berry 268, Marsh Arrow-grass 309.

D   Alpine Marsh Violet 22, Heath Speedweell 25, Water Speedwell 26, Marsh Speedwell 27, Northern Gentian 33, Purple Saxifrage 36, Alpine Bistort 112, Knotgrass 113, Wild Angelica 120, Northern Lovage 121, Caraway 122, Sea-rocket 128, Milky Willowherb 139, Bearberry 148, Bog Rosemary 148B, Autumn Gentian 152, Alsike Clover 155A, Arctic Poppy (pink) 162.

E1   Devil's-bit Scabious 17, Arctic Poppy (white) 162, Iceland Poppy (white) 163, Scheuchzer's Cottongrass 311, Common Cottongrass 338.

E2   Starwort Mouse-ear 84, Three-flowered Rush 317.

E4   Iceland-purslane 111.

E5   Thyme-leaved Speedwell 8, Sea-milkwort 65, Bog Bilberry 69, Small White Orchid 195, Coral-root Orchid 258.

F4   Lesser Bladderwort 212.

G   Stone Bramble 116, Garden Angelica 119, Scottish Asphodel 142, Serrated Wintergreen 151, Northern Bur-reed 207, Floating Bur-reed 208, Sea Arrow-grass 310.

H1b Creeping Bent 279, Whorl-grass 282, Floating Sweet-grass 283, Orange Foxtail 301.

H1c Water Awlwort 137.

H1d Thread-leaved Water-crowfoot

H3b Alpine Meadow-rue 29.

H4   Foliolose Saxifrage 90A.

H5   Iceland-purslane 111, Knotgrass 113, Marsh Pennywort 115, Various-leaved Pondweed 197.

H6   Pigmyweed 137A, Vernal Water-starwort 213, Common Water-starwort 215.

H7b Sea Plantain 250.

H7d Pill Sedge 328, Glacier Sedge 329.

H7e Bulbous Rush 205, Two-flowered Rush 318.

1 Harebell
Campanula rotundifolia

One or two flowers on each stem, rarely more. Corolla bell-shaped, 2-3 cm long, 5-lobed with pointed segments. Calyx glabrous, split 2/3 down, segments linear, 1 cm long or less. Stamens five, one pistil with three stigmas. Stem leafy, at least the lower part. Leaves glabrous, basal leaves heart-shaped or round, long-stalked, slightly crenate. Upper leaves lanceolate to almost linear, entire. **H:** 15-30 cm. **Hab:** Heathland, slopes, grassy meadows and woodland. Common in the East, rare elsewhere. **Sim:** See Arctic Harebell (2). **Fl:** July-August. **I:** Bláklukka. (Bellflower family).

Leaves
(1:1)

2 Arctic Harebell
Campanula uniflora

One flower on each stem, bell dark-blue, smaller and narrower than on harebell, 1.5-1.8 cm long. Calyx hairy, sharply angular, 1-1.2 cm long, split 1/3 down, bluish black or black, segments pointed. Stamens five, one pistil with three stigmas. Leaves glabrous, with lower ones stalked, obovate or oblong, the upper ones sessile, lanceolate or almost linear. **H:** 5-15 cm. **Hab:** Only in high mountains, on grown, more or less rocky mountain flats, preferring ridges with moderate snow cover. Very rare. **Sim:** Harebell (1). The Arctic Harebell differs in size and shape of flowers, hairy calyx, and absence of round basal leaves. **Fl:** July. **I:** Fjallabláklukka. (Bellflower Family).

Leaves
(m. 1.8)

3 Tufted Vetch
Vicia cracca

Many, short-stalked, zygomorphic flowers in one-sided, long-stalked spikes. Corolla about 1 cm long. Calyx hairy, about 4 mm long, split into five narrow, pointed segments. Stamens ten, nine of which are connected into a tube, but one is free. One pistil. Leaves pinnate with 8-10 pairs of oblong, sharp-pointed, pubescent leaflets, terminating in tendrils that wind around stems and twigs of neighbour plants. Stem rather delicate, grooved. **H:** 20-50 cm. **Hab:** Grassland, river banks, meadows, roadsides. Widespread in lowland regions. **Sim:** Bush Vetch (4). The Tufted Vetch is much more frequent, differs through many-flowered, long-stalked clusters, and narrower, more numerous leaflets. **Fl:** July. **I:** Umfeðmingur. (Pea family). — **Marsh Pea** *Lathyrus palustris* is very rare in Iceland and rarely flowers. Racemes are few-flowered, with flowers resembling those of the Tufted Vetch. It differs in having only one to three pairs of linear leaflets.

Leaves with tendrils
(r. 0,6)

28

4 Bush Vetch

■□
□
Vicia sepium

Flowers zygomorphic in one-sided, short-stalked spikes of three or five flowers, similar in shape and size to Tufted Vetch. Calyx slightly hairy, bell-shaped with five acute segments. Leaves pinnate, with 5-8 pairs of leaflets; leaflets oblong-ovate, mucronate, thinly pubescent with terminal leaflets forming tendrils that wind around stems and branches of neighbour plants. Stems slender, furrowed. **H:** 20-40 cm. **Hab:** Meadows and birch-scrub. Very rare. **Sim:** Tufted Vetch (3). The Bush Vetch differs in its short-stalked, few-flowered spikes, lighter-coloured flowers, and abruptly short-pointed leaflets. See also Sea Pea (35). **Fl:** July. **I:** Giljaflækja. (Pea family).

*Pinnate leaf
(r. 0.5)*

5 Nootka Lupin

□■
□
Lupinus nootkatensis

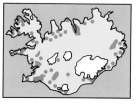

Many-flowered, 20-30 cm long spikes with zygomorphic flowers on 1 cm long, hairy pedicels. Corolla 5-parted, blue or purple, the uppermost petal (banner) with recurved sides, red at the front, with tiny, black spots; lateral wings cover the two lowermost petals, which form the rather tall, bright purple keel. Calyx hairy. Stamens ten, connected into a tube in the lower part, the upper end recurved with bright yellow anthers. Pistil single-styled, forming a 2-5 cm long hairy pod at maturity. Leaves palmate on long petiole, with 7-8 oblanceolate leaflets; petiole and leaflets hairy. **H:** 30-90 cm. **Hab:** River flats, gravel and hillsides with poor soil. Introduced and cultivated to fertilize poor soil and reclaim eroded land. **Sim:** None. **Fl:** June-July. **I:** Lúpína. (Pea family).

*Palmate leaf
(r. 0.3)*

6 Rock Speedwell

□□
■
Veronica fruticans

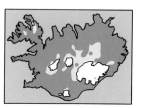

Flowers 1 cm in diameter in few-flowered raceme. Petals appear separate, but are in fact united at the base, and fall off mature flowers in one piece. Petals four, unequal in size, dark blue, with white eyespot in centre, surrounded by a red zone. Stamens two, with white anthers. One, single-styled pistil. Stem leafy, minutely pubescent in upper part, leaves elliptic to narrowly-obovate, obtuse with fine, marginal hairs. **H:** 6-8 cm. **Hab:** Dry or gravelly slopes, cliffs and heathland, preferring sunny habitats. Common. **Sim:** Alpine Speedwell (7). The Rock Speedwell has a larger and more flattened corolla, and is distinguished by red zone in flower, and by smaller and less hairy leaves. Differs from both Arctic Felwort (12) and Alpine Gentian (10) in its 4-parted flowers. **Fl:** June. **I:** Steindepla. (Figwort family).

*Calyx with fruit
(m. 4)*

7 Alpine Speedwell
Veronica alpina

Flowers 3-5 mm wide, dark blue, short-stalked in short raceme. Petals vary in size. Sepals dark blue-green or blackish blue, with white, marginal hairs. Two stamens, one single-styled pistil. Fruit 4-6 mm long, usually glabrous, emarginate with very short (1 mm) style. Stem leafy. Leaves elliptic or obovate, with marginal hairs in lower part, indistinctly dentate, stalkless or short-stalked. **H:** 7-15 cm. **Hab:** Mountain slopes, depressions, along brooklets. Common in mountains, often absent in lowland. **Sim:** Slender Gentian (11) differs from Alpine Speedwell in being entirely hairless. See Rock Speedwell (6). **Fl:** June-July. **I:** Fjalladepla. (Figwort family).

Calyx with fruit (m. 6)

8 Thyme-leaved Speedwell
Veronica serpyllifolia

Many-flowered, long and rather loose raceme. Flowers about 3-5 mm wide. Petals very pale blue, often nearly white with blue nerves. Sepals green, almost hairless, obtuse. Stamens two. One, single-styled pistil, fruit obcordate. Stem leafy. Leaves opposite, ellipsoid or ovate-lanceolate, short-stalked or sessile, indistinctly dentate or almost entire, usually glabrous. **H:** 10-20 cm. **Hab:** Along brooklets, ditches and in moist fields. Common. **Sim:** Easily distinguished from other speedwells by the light, almost white flowers. **Fl:** June. **I:** Lækjadepla. (Figwort family).

Calyx with fruit (m. 4.3)

9 Germander Speedwell
Veronica chamaedrys

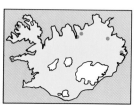

Many-flowered, rather loose racemes growing from upper leaf axils; flowers 10-15 mm wide on 3-8 mm long, slender pedicels. Petals unequal in size, bright blue with darker veins. Sepals green, lanceolate or elliptic, 3-4 mm long, hairy, pointed. Two stamens. One, single-styled pistil. Stem hairy with opposite leaves; leaves ovate, dentate, hairy, 1.5-3 cm long, sessile or short-stalked. **H:** 15-45 cm. **Hab:** Introduced, very rare. **Sim:** Flowers resemble the Rock Speedwell (6), but leaves are quite different, larger and dentate. **Fl:** June-July. **I:** Völudepla. (Figwort family). — **Common Field-speedwell** *Veronica persica* is an introduced weed sometimes found near warm springs in S and SW of Iceland. Flowers are solitary in leaf axils. Petals blue, the lowest one lighter than the others. Leaves short-stalked, ovate or almost round, dentate.

Calyx with fruit (m. 2.5)

32

10 Alpine Gentian
Gentiana nivalis

■
□□

Small, glabrous annual. Flowers 7-8 mm wide, 5-parted. Petals deep blue, pointed at the end making the flowers appear like small starlets. Calyx rather large, 1-2 cm, split 1/3 down into 5, narrow-pointed, dark-keeled segments. Stamens five with yellow-white anthers. Single, pointed pistil with one style. Stem rather slender, angular. Leaves opposite, elliptic to ovate, small (6-9 mm), entire. **H:** 4-12 cm. **Hab:** Heathland and short-grown fields. Common. **Sim:** Slender Gentian (11) is easily identified by its lighter, four-parted flowers, with the calyx cut further down. Arctic Felwort (12) differs from Alpine Gentian in having larger and lighter coloured flower, the calyx much deeper dissected. **Fl:** June-July. **I:** Dýragras. (Gentian family).

Calyx with closed flower (m. 1.2)

11 Slender Gentian
Gentianella tenella

□
■□

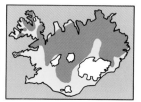

Glabrous annual. Stems usually branched below, slender, dark. Corolla four-parted, split 1/4 to 1/3, light blue or bluish violet, the tube 1 cm long, white appendages in throat of flower. Calyx only half the length of the corolla, split almost all the way down, the segments elliptic or broad-lanceolate. Stamens four to five. One pistil, the fruit a cylindrical capsule, opening at the tip when mature. Leaves opposite, elliptic-ovate, often with bluish tint. **H:** 3-12 cm. **Hab:** Level ground, pastures, river banks. Rather frequent in N of Iceland, esp. towards the interior; rare elsewhere. **Sim:** Alpine Gentian (see 10). Northern Gentian (see 33). Slender Gentian can be distinguished from both by the sepals. **Fl:** June-July. **I:** Maríuvendlingur. (Gentian family).

Calyx with open fruit (m. 2)

12 Arctic Felwort
Lomatogonium rotatum.

□
□■

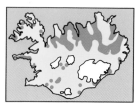

Glabrous annual with few flowers. Corolla five-parted, rather pale blue, 9-15 mm wide. Petals rather broad, pointed, almost free, similar in length or slightly shorter than calyx, which is split almost all the way down, with five, narrow segments of unequal length. Stamens five. Single, blue pistil without style, the stigma forming two stripes on its sides. Stem dark violet. Leaves opposite, lanceolate, 5-20 mm long, sessile. **H:** 8-18 cm. **Hab:** Level ground along rivers, stream banks. Rather frequent in N and E of Iceland, rare elsewhere. **Sim:** Differs from most other five-parted, blue flowers by the pointed petals (see also Alpine Gentian (10)). The stigma stripes are unique. **Fl:** July. **I:** Blástjarna. (Gentian family).

Calyx with flower bud (m. 2)

13 Field Forget-me-not

■☐
☐

Myosotis arvensis

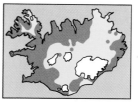

Flowers 4-5 mm wide. Petal segments obtuse, sky-blue with yellow or whitish eye. Flower-buds reddish in a coiled inflorescence which uncoils as the flowers bloom, taking on the ap- pearance of a raceme (false raceme) in fruit. Calyx five-parted, split more than half way down, with white, hooked hairs. Stamens five, hidden in the corolla tube. Fruit-stalks twice as long as calyx, which contains four dark brown, shiny nutlets (schizocarps). Leaves alternate, oblanceolate, 5-7 mm broad, and white-haired like the stem. **H:** 10-30 cm. **Hab:** Grassy slopes, pastures and heaths, usually near populated areas. Common. **Sim:** Water Forget-me-not (14) and Strict Forget-me-not (16). The Field Forget-me-not can be distinguished by its longer pedicels and fruit-stalks (twice the length of calyx). **Fl:** June-July. **I:** Gleym-mér-ei. (Borage family).

Calyx
(m. 3)

14 Water Forget-me-not

☐■
☐

Myosotis scorpioides

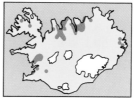

Flowers 7-8 mm wide. Petal segments blunt, sky-blue, with white or yellowish eye. Calyx small, with five rather short lobes. Stamens five; single stigma. Fruits consist of four, brownish black, shiny nutlets (schizocarps). Calyx, stem and leaves sparsely haired with short, appressed hairs. Leaves oblanceolate, 5-15 mm broad. Fruit-stalks only slightly longer than calyx. **H:** 20-40 cm. **Hab:** Naturalized alien, spreading mainly along stream banks and in marshland. **Sim:** Field Forget-me-not (13). The Water Forget-me-not can be distinguished by the short fruit-stalks, larger flowers and sparse, appressed hairs. **Fl:** July. **I:** Engjamunablóm. (Borage family).

Calyx
(m. 3.4)

15 Oysterplant

☐☐
■

Mertensia maritima

Flowers 5-10 mm wide, blue. Corolla bell-shaped, five-parted. Flowerbuds red. Sepals short and broad, triangular, glabrous. Stamens five. Pistil single with one style, the fruit a four-parted schizocarp. Leaves thick, bluish grey, elliptic or obovate, spatulate or nearly round, 10-25 mm broad. **H:** 10-35 cm, but stems and leaves are often prostrate. **Hab:** In sand on the beach. Rather common. **Sim:** Easily identified by bluish, thick leaves, and habitat along the shore. **Fl:** June. **I:** Blálilja. (Borage family).

Calyx with fruit
(m. 3.8)

16 Strict Forget-me-not
Myosotis stricta

Annual. Flowerbuds coiled up in a cyme before opening, uncoiling as flowers open, and then resembling raceme. Flowers only about 2 mm wide, dark blue with white eye. Calyx five-parted, split half way down or more, with hooked hairs. Stamens five. Single pistil, maturing into four-parted schizocarp. Fruit-stalks much shorter than calyx, appressed to the stem. Stem has few lanceolate to narrowly obovate leaves. **H:** Usually 5-10 cm, sometimes more. **Hab:** Dry, gravelly ground and sandy slopes. Rare. **Sim:** Field Forget-me-not (13). The Strict Forget-me-not differs through the very short fruit-stalks (shorter than calyx), and tiny flowers. **Fl:** June-July. **I:** Sandmunablóm. (Borage family). — **Changing Forget-me-not** *Myosotis discolor* is a rare alien in S and SW of Iceland. Resembles the Strict Forget-me-not in its abbreviated fruit-stalks, but these remain extended after flowers are shed and flowers are more whitish or yellowish.

Calyx
(m. 4.8)

17 Devil's-bit Scabious
Succisa pratensis

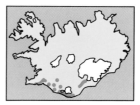

Many flowers in round, compact 1.5-2 cm wide head. Flowers 5-6 mm wide, blue-violet, rarely white, four-parted, with four stamens and a single style. Calyx and corolla white-haired on the outside. Stem long, with only a few leaves. Basal leaves form rosette, lanceolate or elliptic, stalked, rather large, 3-12 cm long and 2-5 cm broad, entire, sparsely haired. **H:** 15-35 cm. **Hab:** Grassy slopes, usually facing south. Common in Mýrdalur and the Eyjafjöll Districts. **Sim:** Field Scabious (17A). **Fl:** July-August. **I:** Stúfa. (Teasel Family). — **Field Scabious** *Knautia arvensis* is rare, introduced only in a few places. Resembles Devil's-bit, but head is more red and flat. Easily distinguished from Devil's-bit by its pinnatifid leaves.

Calyx with fruit
(m. 4.6)

18 Alpine Bartsia
Bartsia alpina

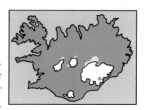

Flowers grow from axils of uppermost leaves, zygomorphic, 1.5-2 cm long. Petal tube slightly curved, dark violet, with glandular hairs. Calyx 5-7 mm long, bell-shaped, dark, split half way down into five segments. Stamens four, equal in length to petals. Pistil covered with appressed, erect hairs. Fruit ovoid, pointed, 1 cm long and 0.5 cm wide, two-cleft at maturity. Leaves nearly stalkless, opposite, ovate, hairy, dentate with blunt teeth; uppermost leaves usually dark violet. **H:** 15-30 cm. **Hab:** Ravines, cliffs, alpine slopes and pastures. Common. **Sim:** None. **Fl:** June-July. **I:** Smjörgras. (Figwort family).

Leaf
(m. 1.2)

19 Pyramidal Bugle
■□ *Ajuga pyramidalis*

Flowers blue, bilabiate. Tube of corolla 10-15 mm long, lower lip four-lobed, upper lip very short, throat hairy. Four stamens, pistil single-styled. Bracts of flower greatly exceed flowers themselves in length (2-3 cm), hairy and densely decussate, making the inflorescence quadrangular in outline. Stem hairy. Leaves 10-15 cm long, hairy, nearly entire, tapering down to the stalk. **H:** 10-15 cm.**Hab:** Birch scrub and among dwarf shrubs in depressions. Very rare. **Sim:** None. Easily recognized by densely decussate bracts of inflorescence, forming four-sided apex. **Fl:** June-July. **I:** Lyngbúi. (Mint family).

Flower in calyx (m. 2)

20 Heath Dog-violet
□■ *Viola canina*

Flowers zygomorphic, nodding. Corolla five-parted. Petals blue, white towards centre of flower, some hairy. White, blunt spur extends back from middle lower petal. Sepals pointed in front, leading downwards to a broad, blunt lobe. Stamens five. Pistil made up of three carpels, forming a rather large capsule at maturity which opens into three segments, loaded with seeds. Leaves long-stalked, narrowly cordate to ovate, denticulate, glabrous. **H:** 8-15 cm. **Hab:** Dry, open slopes, pastures and heathland. Common. **Sim:** Alpine (22), and Northern Marsh Violet (23), Common Dog-violet (20A). The Heath Dog-violet differs from all in narrower leaves tapering to a point. **Fl:** June. **I:** Týsfjóla. (Violet family). — The Heath Dog-violet is divided into two subspecies. Ssp. *montana* (Alpine Dog-violet) is taller, with more upright stems, the stipules larger compared to leaf stalks than on ssp. *canina*. — **Common Dog-violet** *Viola riviniana* resembles Heath Dog-violet, but is rare in Iceland. It has broader, heart-shaped leaves, the spur tapered and more bluish. Found in slopes facing south.

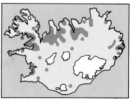

Leaf (1:1)

21 Wild Pansy
□□ *Viola tricolor*
■

Flowers zygomorphic, nodding, 1.5-2.5 cm long, dark violet, yellow or whitish in the centre with dark veins, esp. lowest central petal. Sepals greyish-green or nearly black, the upper end acute, the lower end broader and blunt. Spur dark towards the end. Stamens five. Single-styled pistil of three carpels, capsule 3-parted at maturity. Lowermost leaves nearly round, the upper ones obovate to lanceolate, dentate, short-haired. Stipules large, pinnatifid with large terminal leaflet. **H:** 10-20 cm. **Hab:** Dry gravelly slopes and sand. Common in some districts, recent colonist in others. **Sim:** None. Easily distinguished from other violets by leaf shape and showy flowers. **Fl:** May-June. **I:** Þrenningarfjóla. (Violet family).

Leaf with stipules (r. 0.7)

22 Alpine Marsh Violet
Viola palustris

Prostrate underground stem with ascending flowering branches and petioles; flowers zygomorphic, nodding, smaller than on Heath Dog-violet. Corolla pale violet with darker veins, the spur of the same colour. Sepals almost elliptic, obtuse, with membranous margin. Stamens five, reddish brown. Fruit a three-sided capsule, splitting into three segments at maturity. Tiny bracts in centre of flower scape. Leaves long-petioled, reniform, glabrous, crenate. **H:** 4-8 cm. **Hab:** Moist ground and stream banks. Common. **Sim:** Northern Marsh Violet (23). The Alpine Marsh Violet is best distinguished by location of bracts in about the centre of the flower stem, and reniform, glabrous leaves. Heath Dog-violet (20) can be recognized by its larger flowers and differently shaped leaves. **Fl:** May. **I:** Mýrfjóla. (Violet family).

Leaf
(1:1)

23 Northern Marsh Violet
Viola epípsila

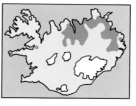

Horizontal underground stem with nodding flowers on erect scapes and leaves on long petioles. Corolla zygomorphic, light violet with dark veins, the spur concoloured with the petals. Sepals green with blunt end and membranous margin. Stamens five, reddish brown. Fruit a three-sided capsule, splitting into three segments at maturity. Tiny bracts in upper part of flower scape. Leaves long-petioled with heart-shaped blade and short, sparse hairs underneath, or on both sides, slightly crenate. **H:** 4-10 cm. **Hab:** Grassy fields, pastures and copsewood. Rather common in NE Iceland. **Sim:** Alpine Marsh Violet (22). The Northern Marsh Violet can be distinguished by location of bracts far above centre of flower scape and heart shaped, slightly hairy leaves; grows in drier grassland than the Alpine Marsh Violet. **Fl:** May-June. **I:** Birkifjóla. (Violet family).

Leaf
(1:1)

24 Common Butterwort
Pinguicula vulgaris

Flowers zygomorphic, nodding, 1-1.5 cm wide. Petals dark violet, connected, with five blunt lobes of unequal length, the lower longer than the upper, with slender, dark spur. Calyx dark with short glandular hairs. Stamens two, single pistil. Leaves form a rosette on the ground, greenish-yellow, entire, 2-3 cm long, tapering to a blunt front end, with involute margin, usually with small flies sticking to the upper surface. **H:** 5-10 cm. **Hab:** Heathland, pastures, moist banks and open ground. Common. **Sim:** The flowers resemble violets, but have connected petals whereas all violets have free petals. The Butterwort can also be easily recognized by the leaves. **Fl:** June. **I:** Lyfjagras. (Bladderwort family).

Flower
(m. 1.8)

25 Heath Speedwell
Veronica officinalis

Stems usually ascending, hairy. Flowers in many-flowered racemes in upper leaf axils, on short pedicels, 4-6 mm wide, four-parted. Petals light blue with darker veins. Calyx four-lobed with glandular hairs. Stamens two. Single pistil, forming heart-shaped fruit at maturity with long, curved style. Stem hairy. Leaves opposite, ovate or elliptic, 2-7 cm long and 1.5-3.5 cm broad, short-stalked, hairy, dentate, teeth of different size. **H:** 20-40 cm. **Hab:** Grassy slopes, sheltered locations and birch copses. Common in some districts, esp. in the SW and in some coastal areas in the N and E of Iceland. **Sim:** More hairy than other speedwells, and differs also through large, coarsely toothed leaves. **Fl:** July. **I:** Hárdepla. (Figwort family).

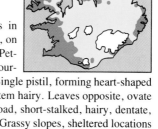

Calyx with fruit (m. 3.5)

26 Blue Water-speedwell
Veronica anagallis-aquatica

Stems erect or floating in water. Flowers 4-5 mm wide in racemes in leaf axils. Pedicels 3-6 mm long, with short glandular hairs. Corolla light violet with four, unequal-sized petals. Sepals green, broad-elliptic, 2-3 mm long. Stamens two. One, single-styled pistil; the fruit slightly shorter than the sepals. Leaves opposite, ovate or broad-elliptic, 2-8 cm long, entire or indistinctly dentate-crenate, almost glabrous, stalkless. **H:** 20-50 cm. **Hab:** Warm springs and creeks. Rare, found only in the SW. **Sim:** Differs from other speedwells by opposite flower racemes, glabrous, large-leaved stems. **Fl:** July-August. **I:** Laugadepla. (Figwort family).

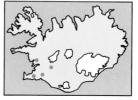

Calyx with fruit (m. 4.7)

27 Marsh Speedwell
Veronica scutellata

Prostrate stems with opposite, 10-20 mm long, lanceolate-linear, pointed, entire and smooth leaves. Flowers on long pedicels, in branched, alternate inflorescences in axils of upper leaves. Flowers 3-4 mm wide, pale violet with four petals. Sepals green, elliptic. Two stamens. One, single-styled pistil, the fruits heart-shaped. **H:** Stems 10-20 cm long, prostrate. **Hab:** Moist ground along lakes and ponds, and on the bottom of pools which dry up late in summer. Rather common. **Sim:** Some speedwells have similar flowers. Marsh Speedwell differs by the narrow leaves and completely prostrate stems. **Fl:** July. **I:** Skriðdepla. (Figwort family).

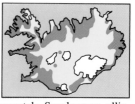

Calyx with fruit (m. 4.5)

28 Selfheal
Prunella vulgaris

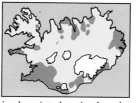

Many flowers in stubby, 2 cm long raceme, zygomorphic, on short pedicels. Petals connected, corolla violet, with helmet-shaped upper lip. Calyx bell-shaped, slightly compressed, dark reddish violet with five unequal-sized, pointed, veined teeth. Stamens four, the pistil maturing into a four-parted schizocarp on bottom of calyx. Stem quadrangular. Leaves opposite, ovate to broad-lanceolate, with distant teeth or entire, thin-haired, the lower leaves long-stalked, the upper ones short-petioled and seated just below the inflorescence. **H:** 8-20 cm. **Hab:** Grassy, sheltered places, slopes, birch copses, often in warm soil around hot springs. Common in warmer districts of the country, elsewhere only in geothermal soil. **Sim:** None. **Fl:** June-July. **I:** Blákolla. (Mint family).

Flower (m. 3)

29 Alpine Meadow-rue
Thalictrum alpinum

Flowers small in rather thin terminal raceme on stem. Perianth simple, violet. Perianth leaves elliptic, ca. 2 mm long. Stamens 8, long, hanging out of flower, anthers first yellow, then brown, 2 mm long. Pistils two to six, bottle-shaped, with curved stigma. Fruits are nuts, inflated and longitudinally striate, on nodding pedicel. Leaves bipinnate, long-petioled, the leaflets dark green and shiny on top, light greyish green underneath with revolute margin. **H:** 6-20 cm. **Hab:** Heathland, slopes and pastures. Common. **Sim:** None. **Fl:** May-June. **I:** Brjóstagras. (Buttercup family).

Flower (m. 6)

30 Wood Crane's-bill
Geranium sylvaticum

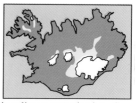

Flowers five-parted, large, 1.5-2.5 cm wide. Corolla violet with free petals. Sepals green with broad transparent margin, glandular, with 2-3 mm long terminal point. Stamens ten. One style with five-parted stigma. Long-beaked fruit splits at maturity into five strips curling up from below when seeds are ripe. Stem furrowed. Basal leaves long-petioled, hairy, palmatifid, the lobes deeply dissected into dentate segments. **H:** 20-50 cm. **Hab:** Grassy slopes, sheltered locations, ravines, birch copses, snowbeds in the lower mountains. Common. **Sim:** None. **Fl:** June. **I:** Blágresi. (Cranesbill family). — The Wood Crane's-bill belongs to the undergrowth of birch woods, and must have had wider distribution when birches and willows formed copsewood throughout the country. In deforested areas it has survived in depressions covered by snow in winter.

Leaf (r. 0.32)

31 Serrate Gentian
Gentianella detonsa

Glabrous annual. Corolla tubular, 2.5-5 cm long, 1-1.5 cm wide in upper part, violet-blue, usually four-parted, but occasionally five-parted, without appendages in the throat, twisted or screwed before it opens. Calyx 2-3 cm long, usually with four long, narrow lobes. Stamens four, one pistil of two carpels, maturing into an oblong, round capsule. Stem strict, furrowed, usually with many side-branches below, which are upright and almost as long as main stem. Leaves narrowly obovate or lanceolate, entire, 2-3 cm long. **H:** 10-20 cm. **Hab:** Level river banks and plains, often near seashore. Widespread except on southern coast. **Sim:** Field Gentian (32). The Serrate Gentian has more bluish flowers, lacking the white appendages in the throat, and has a quite different calyx. **Fl:** July-August. **I:** Engjavöndur. (Gentian family).

Calyx with fruit (1:1)

32 Field Gentian
Gentianella campestris

Corolla tubular below, about 2-2.5 cm long, violet, the petal lobes with hair-like, white appendages on inner side. Calyx split almost to the base, the two outer lobes very broad (5-7 mm), the inner ones quite narrow. Four stamens, one pistil with two-parted stigma. Stem strict, furrowed or winged, glabrous, usually branched in the upper part. Leaves ovate to ovate-lanceolate, usually 2-3 cm long, glabrous, entire. **H:** 10-18 cm. **Hab:** Dry soil on grassy ground or slopes. Rather common. **Sim:** Serrate Gentian (31) and Autumn Gentian (152). The Field Gentian differs in its two broad sepals, also in its bright violet flowers, and usually dark violet-tinted leaves and stems. **Fl:** July-August. **I:** Maríuvöndur. (Gentian family).

Calyx and corolla (m. 1.4)

33 Northern Gentian
Gentianella aurea

Flowers usually crowded just above two large leaves. Corolla rather small, 4-5 mm wide, and 7-8 mm long, pale violet in upper part, often greenish white below. Petal lobes four (or five), pointed, with no appendages. Sepal lobes slightly shorter, narrow (1 mm), unequal in size. Four stamens, single pistil. Stems usually branched in lower part, sharply quadrangular or winged, hairless. Leaves entire, ovate, pointed at apex, broad in lower part. **H:** 8-12 cm. **Hab:** Sandy grassland, slopes, hillsides and heathland. Common. **Sim:** Slender Gentian (11). Northern Gentian differs in its lighter, more violet-coloured, crowded flowers and shorter petal tube. Autumn Gentian (see 152). **Fl:** June-July. **I:** Gullvöndur. (Gentian family).

Calyx with fruit (m. 2)

48

34 Blue Heath
Phyllodoce coerulea

Flowers at the end of 1-3 cm long, dark red pedicels. Corolla gamopetalous, bell-shaped, but wider in the centre with narrow opening, 7-9 mm long, 4-5 mm wide, reddish-violet with five very short petal-lobes. Sepals dark red, glandular, oblong-triangular, pointed, 3-4 mm long. Stems ascending, woody below, leafy in upper part. Leaves evergreen, linear, with blunt end, 4-7 mm long and 1 mm broad, minutely denticulate. **H:** 8-15 cm, sometimes more. **Hab:** Shrubby slopes and heathland. Rare. **Sim:** Crowberry (268). The Blue Heath is very similar when not in flower, but leaves are slightly larger and thinner. **Fl:** June-July. **I:** Bláklukkulyng. (Heath family). — The Blue Heath is one of the more striking and rare plants in Iceland. Its distribution is restricted to the outer districts on both sides of Eyjafjörður, where snow covers the ground throughout the winter, and to the area around Loðmundarfjörður in the East.

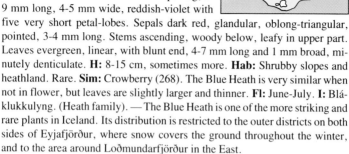

Flower (m. 2.4)

35 Sea Pea
Lathyrus japonicus ssp. *maritimus*

Flowers zygomorphic, 2-2.5 cm long, usually two to four in raceme on long stalk in leaf axils. Petals 5, the uppermost forming large, recurved standard, more than 1 cm broad. Calyx 8-9 mm long, with five, pointed lobes. Stamens ten. One pistil which matures into a large, flat pod; the pod 4-7 cm long, with long-pointed apex. Leaves pinnate, with three to four pairs of leaflets; the leaflets ovate to elliptic, 15-20 mm long and 5-10 mm broad, the terminal leaflet and the next pair usually converted to tendrils. Stipules shaped like a distorted heart or triangle, usually 1 cm broad, and 1.5 cm long. Pods flat, 4-7 cm long, pointed. **H:** 15-25 cm. **Hab:** Sandy soil, usually near the seashore, occasionally in cliffs. Rather rare. **Sim:** Bush Vetch (4). The Sea Pea differs in its larger and more red flowers, fewer and broader leaflets. **Fl:** July. **I:** Baunagras. (Pea family). — The Sea Pea fixes nitrogen from the air with the aid of bacteria found in root nodules. It helps to restore the nitrogen supply of the soil like many other species of the pea family. Large, green, round patches of grass may sometimes be seen in sand-dunes near the sea, for instance in Hornstrandir in NW of Iceland, where the Sea Pea has established itself. It is palatable to sheep but vulnerable to continuous grazing.

Leaf with stipules (r. 0.9)

36 Purple Saxifrage
Saxifraga oppositifolia

Flowers 10-15 cm wide, five-parted. Corolla has free petals, red or reddish-violet. Sepals obtuse, 4-5 mm long, ciliate. Stamens ten. Pistil pink or reddish, the upper part divided, with two styles. The leafy shoots densely covered with short, decussate leaves, thus appearing quadrangular. Leaves 3-4 mm long, obovate, thick, involute, evergreen, ciliate, tipped with white, calciferous gland. **H:** Shoots are decumbent, often 5-20 cm long. **Hab:** Cliffs, gravelly hills, rock outcrops. Common. **Sim:** Moss Campion (60). The Purple Saxifrage differs in its quadrangular leaf shoots and divided pistil. **Fl:** April-May, occasionally end of March. **I:** Vetrarblóm. (Saxifrage family).

Leafy shoot m. 6)

37 Heath Spotted Orchid
Dactylorhiza maculata

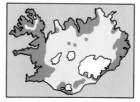

Flowers in raceme, purple, zygomorphic, five of the petals directed upwards forming upper lip, the largest bent down to form the lower lip. Lower lip has dark red spots and stripes, three-lobed, with one narrow central lobe and two broad lateral lobes. Pistil furrowed and twisted, located below the epigynous perianth. Stem leafy. Leaves lanceolate, large (6-10 cm long and 1-2 cm broad), clasping the stem, glabrous, with brown-spotted upper side, the upper leaves smaller. **H:** 15-25 cm. **Hab:** Birch copses, grass and heather slopes. Frequent in some districts, rare or absent in others. **Sim:** None. **Fl:** June-July. **I:** Brönugrös. (Orchid family).

Flower (m. 2)

38 Creeping Thistle
Cirsium arvense

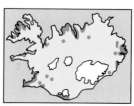

Tall, branched perennial, topped with many dense-flowered, purple heads, each sitting on swollen, ovate knob, covered with dark grey, overlapping, appressed bracts, with reddish, recurved tip. Corolla tubular, curved. Stems furrowed, spiny. Leaves pinnately incised, clasping, 5-12 cm long, the lobes irregularly dentate with spines, the lower side covered with greyish white woolly hair. **H:** 30-70 cm. **Hab:** Roadsides and rubbish dumps. Rather rare, but naturalized alien, growing in dense, long-lasting stands. **Sim:** None, easily recognized by the spiny leaves. **Fl:** August-Sept. **I:** Þistill. (Daisy family).

Leaf (r. 0.4)

39 Red Dead-nettle

Lamium purpureum

Flowers many growing in upper leaf axils. Corolla 10-15 mm long, zygomorphic, purplish or red, hairy on the outside, bilabiate. Calyx split half way down into five lobes. Sepal lobes narrow-pointed, subulate, hairy, divergent. Stamens four, single-styled pistil with divided stigma. Stem quadrangular. Leaves opposite, stalked, heart- or reniform, varying in size (1-4 cm), coarsely dentate with blunt teeth, the upper leaves close. **H:** 15-30 cm. **Hab:** Waste places, gardens and home-fields. Rather rare alien. **Sim:** Several other alien dead-nettles with purple flowers occur in populated areas. **Henbit** *Lamium amplexicaule* has more rounded leaves, the upper ones stalkless, clasping the stem. **Northern Dead-nettle** *Lamium molucellifolium* has reniform leaves, the calyx with longer sepal lobes. **Fl:** June-July. **I:** Akurtvítönn. (Mint family).

Flower (m. 2)

40 Alpine Catchfly

Lychnis alpina

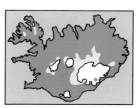

Flowers crowded in 1.5-2 cm wide inflorescence on top of stem. Individual flowers 5-parted, 1 cm long. Petals purplish red, two-lobed. Calyx bell-shaped, sepals connected at the base, with five blunt lobes, red like the bracts of the flowers. Stamens ten, one 5-styled pistil. Stem with opposite, lanceolate, pointed, reddish or green leaves. **H:** 6-15 cm. **Hab:** Dry hillsides, open places and gravelly soil. Common. **Sim:** Thrift (61). The Alpine Catchfly differs in the leafy stem, usually darker flowers, and terminal notch in the petals. **Fl:** July. **I:** Ljósberi. (Pink family). — **Ragged Robin** *Lychnis flos-cuculi* is related to Alpine Catchfly, but much taller (20-60 cm), with fewer and larger flowers, the petals deeply four-lobed. Found in Mýrdalur and Eyjafjöll districts (S. Iceland), rare elsewhere.

Fruit in calyx (m. 3)

41 Wild Thyme

Thymus praecox ssp. *arcticus*

Flowers close together on branch tips and in uppermost leaf axils. Corolla red, 5-parted, bilabiate. Petal lobes obtuse, two forming the upper lip and three the lower. Calyx also bilabiate, hairy, with pointed segments. Stamens four, two longer and two shorter. One single-styled pistil of two carpels. Stem quadrangular, hairy on two opposite sides, or all around. Leaves small, 3-5 mm long, opposite, spatulate or obovate, coarsely ciliate in basal part. **H:** Stems decumbent, upright branches 2-5 cm. **Hab:** Gravel hills, dry heathland and slopes, cliffsides and rock ledges. Very common. **Sim:** None. **Fl:** June-July. **I:** Blóðberg. (Mint family).

Flower (m. 6.5)

42 Great Burnet
Sanguisorba officinalis

Flowers crowded in dense, 1-3 cm long and 1 cm wide capitate and terminal clusters on branch tips, epigynous. Petals dark red, elliptic, 3-4 mm long. Sepals light brown. Stamens four, one pistil with curved style. Stem furrowed. Leaves pinnate, usually with three to six pairs of leaflets; leaflets glabrous, light bluish green underneath, darker on top, serrate, obtuse, with cordate base on short petiole. **H:** 15-50 cm. **Hab:** Grassy slopes in gorges and steep hillsides. Native in some heathlands of the Southwest, elsewhere only as an alien around farms and in villages. **Sim:** None. **Fl:** July. **I:** Blóðkollur. (Rose family).

Leaf
(r. 0.6)

43 Rosebay Willowherb
Epilobium angustifolium

Flowers 2 cm wide, crowded in long raceme. Petals red, obovate. Sepals dark red, lanceolate, hairy. Stamens eight. Inferior, long and soft-haired pistil. Leaves opposite, lanceolate, entire or indistinctly dentate, without hairs, 4-12 cm long and 1-2 cm broad. **H:** 30-70 cm. **Hab:** Common as alien in villages and towns, forming dense stands by means of creeping stolons. Native in cliffsides or woodland, flowering late. Occasionally found in poor soil in rather dry hillsides facing south where it forms dwarfish, 10-20 cm long, leafy shoots, not flowering unless transplanted to fertile soil. Rather rare. **Sim:** Easily recognized by long inflorescences with large, four-parted flowers. **Fl:** July-August. **I:** Sigurskúfur. (Willowherb family).

Leaf
(r. 0.5)

44 Arctic Riverbeauty
Epilobium latifolium

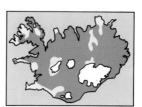

Flowers large, four-parted, 3-4 cm wide. Petals red, obovate. Sepals dark red, lanceolate, pointed, thin- and short-haired. Stamens eight. One long (3-6 cm), soft-haired, red pistil made up of four carpels. The long pistil resembles a thick pedicel underneath the epigynous flower. Leaves opposite, lanceolate, 20-40 mm long and 4-10 mm broad, short-haired, entire or with few, indistinct teeth. **H:** 15-25 cm. **Hab:** Gravelly, flat riversides, often covering wide stretches. Occasionally on cliffsides in mountain slopes, or river gorges. Rather common. **Sim:** Rosebay Willowherb (43). The Arctic Riverbeauty is easily recognized by its much larger and fewer flowers. **Fl:** July. **I:** Eyrarrós. (Willowherb family).

Leaf
(1:1)

56

45 Chickweed Willowherb
Epilobium alsinifolium

Flowers red, 4-parted, 8-10 mm long. Calyx half the length of the corolla, red or greenish. Stamens eight. Single, smooth pistil made up of four carpels beneath the perianth; the mature fruit 3-7 cm long, opening into four strips. Seeds have tuft of white hairs. Leaves opposite, ovate, acute, dentate, glabrous, 2-3.5 cm long and 1-2 cm broad. Stem quadrangular, with two longitudinal hair stripes. Underground stolons with yellow scale leaves growing from base. **H:** 10-30 cm. **Hab:** Cold springs, along spring-water creeks and ditches. Common. **Sim:** Hornemann's Willowherb (46). The Chickweed Willowherb is a stronger plant with more acute leaves, larger flowers, usually with stolons at the base. The Marsh Willowherb (49) has similar flowers, but much narrower leaves. **Fl:** June-July. **I:** Lindadúnurt. (Willowherb family).

Leaf
(m. 1.3)

46 Hornemann's Willowherb
Epilobium hornemanni

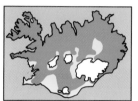

Flowers red, four-parted, 5-7 mm long. Calyx about half the length of the corolla, red or greenish. Stamens eight. One red, glabrous pistil of four carpels, 2.5-4 cm long, splitting into four strips at maturity. Seeds have long tuft of white hairs. Stem quadrangular, hairy on two opposite sides. Leaves opposite, ovate or elliptic, usually with blunt end, indistinctly dentate or entire, glabrous, 1-2.5 cm long and 0.5-1.2 cm broad. **H:** 8-15 cm. **Hab:** Along streams, moist snowbeds, mossy springwater soil. Common, though rare in lowland districts. **Sim:** Chickweed Willowherb (45). The Hornemann's Willowherb differs through shorter stolons, smaller flowers, and less toothed leaves with obtuse ends. Milky Willowherb (139) differs through white flowers and lighter, yellowish green stem and leaves. **Fl:** June-July. **I:** Heiðadúnurt. (Willowherb family).

Leaf
(m. 2)

47 American Willowherb
Epilobium watsonii

Flowers red. Corolla 8-12 mm long. Calyx 3-4 mm long, dark red. Stamens eight. Pistil inferior, 2-6 cm long, with simple, clavate stigma, the mature fruit opening into four strips, the seeds with tuft of long white hairs. Stem furrowed, short-haired. Leaves narrowly ovate or elliptic, finely denticulate, stalkless, 3-7 cm long, 1-2.5 cm broad, opposite on lower part of stem, often alternate on upper part. **H:** 30-80 cm. **Hab:** Foreign species naturalized in ditches, roadsides, grassland or dumps, mainly in and around Reykjavík. **Sim:** Broad-leaved Willowherb (see 47A). **Fl:** July. **I:** Vætudúnurt. (Willowherb family). — **Broadleaved Willowherb** *Epilobium montanum* is a very rare alien resembling American Willowherb, but differing through the stigma, which is divided into four segments, and through the short-petioled, more coarsely dentate leaves.

Leaf
(r. 0.8)

48 Cliff Willowherb
■□
Epilobium collinum
□

Flowers red or pink, 7-8 mm long. Calyx red or green. Stamens eight. Stigma split into four segments, the pistil 2-3 cm long, hairy, inferior. Stem round, hairy all around. Leaves opposite, ovate to ovate-lanceolate, obtuse, distinctly dentate, the upper leaves often hairy on lower side, esp. the midrib. **H:** 6-12 cm. **Hab:** Cliffs, hillsides and gorges, esp. on the sunny side. Found here and there in S of Iceland, rather rare elsewhere. **Sim:** Differs from other willowherbs (45-50) in the round stem equally hairy on all sides, sharper teeth, blunt-tipped leaves, and 4-parted stigma, clearly visible in sunshine, when flowers are wide open. **Fl:** July. **I:** Klappadúnurt. (Willowherb family).

Leaf
(m. 2.8)

49 Marsh Willowherb
□■
Epilobium palustre
□

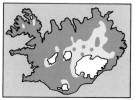

Flowers red; petals 7-9 mm long. Calyx shorter, red or green. Stamens four. Single, hairy pistil, 4-6 cm long, with four carpels and whole, clavate stigma; splits up into four strips at maturity. Seeds with white tuft of hairs. Stem round, fairly evenly hairy all around. Leaves opposite, narrow-lanceolate, entire or with distant, indistinct teeth, 2-4 cm long, 3-7 mm broad, slightly hairy, at least the upper ones. Plant forms slender, prostrate stolons late in the fall, with terminal, red bulbs. **H:** 12-30 cm. **Hab:** Among sedges in bogs, ditches, moist soil. Common. **Sim:** Differs from all other willowherbs (45-50) in the narrow, entire leaves, and its habitat in bogs rather than springs. **Fl:** July-August. **I:** Mýradúnurt. (Willowherb family).

Leaf and open fruit
(r. 0.7)

50 Alpine Willowherb
□□
Epilobium anagallidifolium
■■

Flowers red, 5-7 mm wide. Calyx usually dark red. Stamens four. One pistil with four carpels and unsplit stigma; the pistil, located beneath the epigynous flower, splits into four strips at maturity. Seeds with white tuft of hairs. Stem hairy on two opposite sides, usually bent like a hook at flowering time, stretches to almost upright position when fruit matures. Leaves opposite, obovate, elliptic or lanceolate, usually with blunt end, 1-1.5 cm long and 3-6 mm broad, slightly dentate, or entire. **H:** 3-6 cm. **Hab:** Snowbeds, moist depressions. Common at higher altitudes, rare or absent in the lowland of snow-poor districts. **Sim:** Other willowherbs (45-49). The Alpine Willowherb is smaller, and usually recognizable by the curved stem. **Fl:** June-July. **I:** Fjalladúnurt. (Willowherb family).

Leaf
(m. 4)

51 Marsh Cinquefoil
Potentilla palustris

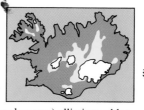

Flowers five-parted. Sepals large (8-12 mm), dark red, acute. Petals much shorter (4-5 mm), red and pointed. Stamens numerous with dark red anthers. Many small pistils on elevated re-

ceptacle. Leaves opposite, pinnate with five (rarely seven) elliptic to oblan-ceolate and clearly dentate leaflets which are so close as to make the compound leaves appear palmate rather than pinnate, light greyish-green and hairy below, the stipules long, coherent to the petiole half way up. **H:** 15-25 cm. **Hab:** Moist pastures, meadows and bogs. Common. **Sim:** None. The Marsh Cinquefoil can be easily recognized both by flowers and leaves. **Fl:** June. **I:** Engjarós. (Rose family).

Compound leaf (r. 0.4)

52 Hemp-nettle
Galeopsis tetrahit

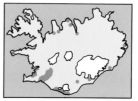

Flowers crowded in leaf axils, zygomorphic. Corolla 12-18 mm long, purple with white hairs, bilabiate, tubular below, curved in upper part. Calyx split half way down or more into

five spiny bristles. Stamens four, the pistil maturing into four-parted schizocarp in bottom of calyx. Stem quadrangular, hairy. Leaves opposite, stalked, the blade ovate to rhomboidal, coarsely dentate, 2-5 cm long, hairy on both sides. **H:** 15-30 cm. **Hab:** Alien in gardens, villages and farms. Rare. **Sim:** Red Dead-nettle (39). The Hemp-nettle differs in the coarse hairs and acutely pointed leaves. **Fl:** July. **I:** Garðahjálmgras. (Mint family).

Leaf (1:1)

53 Strict Primrose
Primula stricta

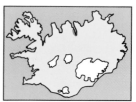

Several flowers in corymb at the end of un-branched stem. Flower tube 7-8 mm long with expanded limb consisting of five pink-red lobes, each with a terminal notch. Calyx 4-5 mm long, split 1/4 down, greenish, finely dark-spotted in upper part. Stamens five, shorter than the flower-tube. One pistil. Pedicels 5-10 mm long, with short, narrow bracts at the base. Stem without leaves or hairs; the leaves in basal rosette, spatulate, 1-2 cm long, tapering to the petiole. **H:** 10-20 cm. **Hab:** Moist, bare or short-grown ground, esp. on thin soil over rock ledges; also on river banks. Very rare. **Sim:** None. **Fl:** May-June. **I:** Maríulykill. (Primrose family). — **Greenland Primrose** *Primula egaliksensis* has been found in one locality in Iceland. It is shorter than the Strict Primrose, with white flowers, the calyx split 1/3 down, deeper than on Strict Primrose.

Inflorescence (m. 1.5)

54 Small Cranberry
■■
☐ *Vaccinium microcarpum*

Flowers 6-7 mm wide, four-parted, nodding on
1-1.5 cm long, red pedicel; in centre of pedicel
are two tiny bracts one slightly above the other.
Corolla deeply divided; petals connected at the
base, bright red, lobes 4-5 mm long, becoming reflexed. Calyx red with short
lobes. Stamens eight, densely packed and protruding far out of the flower; filaments hairy, dark brown; anthers oblong, light brown. One pistil with long,
red, persistent style. Fruit is a red berry, 5-7 mm in diameter. Leafy shoots
prostrate, with alternate, distant leaves; the leaves narrowly cordate to ovate,
3-4 mm long and 1.5-2 mm broad, dark green or slightly reddish on top, on
short petiole, evergreen, with revolute margin and raised midrib on lower
side. **H:** Prostrate, shoot length 10-20 cm or more. **Hab:** Hummocks in bogs,
usually among *Sphagnum* or other mosses. Rare. **Sim:** Easily recognized by
flower or fruit; flowerless shoots resemble thin-leaved Crowberry branches
(268). The Small Cranberry has broader leaves and the lower side of the leaves
differs distinctly from Crowberry. **Fl:** June-July. **I:** Mýraberjalyng. (Heath
family).

Leaf, lower side
(m. 7)

55 Trailing Azalea
☐☐ *Loiseleuria procumbens*
■

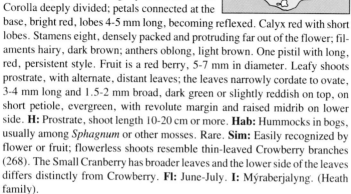

Flowers 4-6 mm wide. Petals connected at the
base, split midway down into five (six) separate
lobes, pink to bright red. Calyx dark red,
deeply dissected with blunt-tipped lobes. Sta-
mens 5-8 with dark anthers. One, single-styled pistil with two or three locules,
developing into capsule at maturity. Stems woody. Leaves opposite, 6-7 mm
long, short-stalked, 1-2 mm broad, evergreen, rigid, shiny on top, with revolute margin and thick midrib on lower side, and only a narrow slot on both
sides between midrib and raised margin; a single furrow on upper side above
midrib. **H:** Stems ascending, the erect part usually 5-10 cm. **Hab:** Dwarf-
shrub heath, often on low hilltops or exposed slopes. Rather common. **Sim:**
When not in flower the Trailing Azalea may bear a slight resemblance to
Crowberry (268), but still more to Diapensia (93). The leaves of the Trailing
Azalea differ by the double slot on the lower side, and by the more elliptic
shape of the leaves. Easily recognized in flower. Colour of flowers is particu-
larly resistant when dried. **Fl:** June. **I:** Sauðamergur. (Heath family).

Fruit in calyx
(m. 8)

56 Water avens
■□
Geum rivale

Flowers large, 1.5-2 cm wide, usually 5-parted. Petals first a creamy yellow, then pinkish red with darker veins, the lower part tapering to a narrow claw, the upper part broad, retuse. Sepals dark red, hairy, triangular, alternating with linear, revolute epicalyx lobes. Stamens numerous with yellow anthers. Many pistils, each with a hairy style, elongating to a beak on mature fruit. Stem rises from stout rhizome. Stem leaves three-lobed, with dentate segments and stipules, basal leaves on long petioles, pinnate, with very unequal lateral leaflets and large, deeply incised terminal leaflet. All leaflets and stipules coarsely dentate, hairy. **H:** 25-40 cm. **Hab:** Grassy heathland of moderate moisture, hillsides. Common. **Sim:** None. **Fl:** June-July. **I:** Fjalldalafífill. (Rose Family).

Pinnate leaf (m. 4)

57 Red Clover
□■
Trifolium pratense

Flowers zygomorphic, in many-flowered, ovoid to round, 2.5-3 cm broad heads. Corolla red, 12-16 mm long. Calyx 7-8 mm, with appressed hairs, split half way down into five linear segments with long, bristle-like hairs, tubular below. Stamens ten, single pistil. Leaves alternate, mostly basal, palmate, with three, obovate to ellipsoid, 2-3.5 cm long, thin-haired leaflets. Stipules form membranous to light green, dark-veined sheath, terminating in long bristle. **H:** 20-40 cm. **Hab:** Grassy pastures and cultivated homefields, introduced and partly naturalized. Rather rare. **Sim:** Alsike Clover (155A) which has nearly or entirely white flower heads. The Red Clover differs also through the appressed-haired calyx; on Alsike Clover and White Clover the calyx is almost without hairs. **Fl:** July-Aug. **I:** Rauðsmári. (Pea Family).

Stipule (m. 2)

58 Hairy Stonecrop
□□
■
Sedum villosum

Flowers 6-10 mm wide, five-parted, usually two or three at the top of each stem. Petals pinkish red, pointed, 5-7 mm long. Sepals only half the length of the petals, with glandular hairs. Stamens ten. Pistils five, each with one style, forming small, curved fruits, splitting laterally below the terminal beak. Stem has alternate, reddish or red-spotted, thick and fleshy, 4-6 mm long and nearly cylindrical leaves. **H:** 3-8 cm. **Hab:** Open, moist soil and gravelly, moist streamsides. Common. **Sim:** None. Other stonecrops are yellow-flowered. **Fl:** June. **I:** Flagahnoðri. (Stonecrop Family).

Fruits (m. 6)

66

59 Heather
Calluna vulgaris

Flowers short-stalked, in racemes, four-parted, about 3 mm wide. Pinkish red colour is due to the sepals, which are elliptic, and exceed the petals in length. Ciliate, dark reddish green bracts support base of calyx. Stamens eight; single, red-styled pistil; the fruit an almost spherical capsule. Leaves evergreen, densely decussate, only 2 mm long and 0.5 mm broad, making the branches appear quadrangular. Leafy shoot usually protrudes through the flower raceme. **H:** Stems are prostrate with ascending branches about 10-20 cm tall. **Hab:** Heathland and slopes. Common. **Sim:** None. **Fl:** August-Sept. **I:** Beitilyng. (Heath family). — Heather has evergreen shoots, and has been of some use for winter grazing. It adorns its surroundings with the bright pink flowers appearing late in the season, when other plants exhibit their fall costume.

Flower (m. 7)

60 Moss Campion
Silene acaulis

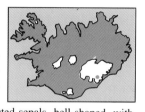

Plant forms compact, rounded, often hemispherical tussocks that bristle with leafy shoots and short-stalked flowers. Corolla with free petals, reddish to pink, 8-10 mm wide. Petals obtuse or slightly notched. Calyx with connected sepals, bell-shaped, with five, short, rounded lobes, reddish in upper part, green below. Stamens ten. One three-styled pistil; fruit a cylindrical capsule. Leaves in rosettes, linear, 5-15 mm long, 1-2 mm broad, sharp-pointed with tiny teeth or hairs on margin. **H:** The hummocks are often 15-40 cm across, their height 5-10 cm. **Hab:** Sandy or gravelly, usually dry soil, exposed locations on hills and rock ledges, poor pastures. Very common. **Sim:** Purple Saxifrage (36). The Moss Campion differs in its longer and more linear leaves, and by the tussock formation; the leaves have no terminal white gland like the Purple Saxifrage. **Fl:** May-June. **I:** Lambagras. (Pink family). — The round tussocks formed by the Moss Campion are peculiar and mark eroded hills in the spring, when they are covered with pink flowers. Deep and solid taproot extends down from the tussock. In the past it was used as food in times of famine.

Fruit in calyx (m. 3.7)

61 Thrift
Armeria maritima

Flowers crowded in a compact head, 1.5-2 cm in diameter. Individual flowers pink, 6-10 mm wide; petals obtuse. Calyx funnel-shaped, hairy in lower part, with five red ribs connected by transparent membrane, the ribs terminating in five teeth. Stamens five. One 5-styled pistil, the styles with white hair at the base. Membranous, yellowish brown bracts at base of head. Stem without leaves, short-haired. Leaves all in basal rosettes, linear, 15-50 mm long and 0.5-1 mm broad. **H:** 6-18 cm. **Hab:** Sand, gravel and eroded land, sometimes in dry grassland or heaths. Very common, not least in the interior deserts. **Sim:** Alpine Catchfly (40). The Thrift differs in the leafless stem and entire petals. The Alpine Catchfly has opposite leaves on the stem and split petals. **Fl:** June. **I:** Geldingahnappur. (Sealavender family).

Individual flower (m. 3.2)

62 Lady Smock
Cardamine nymanii

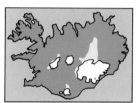

Flowers form short, dense corymb on top of stem. Petals pink to pale-violet, with darker veins, 10-15 mm long, with rounded or slightly notched end, tapering to narrow claw below. Sepals green, 3-4 mm long. Stamens six. One pistil, maturing into 2-3.5 cm long and 1-1.5 mm broad silique. Stem glabrous. Leaves pinnate; basal leaves with round leaflets, the terminal leaflet usually larger, the stem-leaves with narrow, lanceolate to linear leaflets. **H:** 15-35 cm. **Hab:** Meadows, moist pastures and bogs. Common. **Sim:** None. **Fl:** May-June. **I:** Hrafnaklukka. (Mustard family).

Basal leaf and stem-leaf (r. 0.5)

63 Common Valerian
Valeriana officinalis

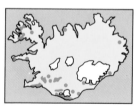

Tall plant with many 5-parted flowers in umbellate inflorescences. Corolla funnel-shaped, pink, the petals connected below, with five, rounded lobes. Sepals 2-3 mm long, hairy, acute, with red stripes and membranous margin, usually dentate. Stamens three. One single-styled pistil with three-parted stigma. Stem furrowed. Leaves opposite, pinnate, with lanceolate to ovate, dentate, hairy leaflets; the basal leaves on long stalk with 6-8 pairs of leaflets. **H:** 40-80 cm. **Hab:** Fertile, south-facing slopes and woodland. Rather rare in natural habitats, commonly cultivated in gardens. **Sim:** Hill Valerian (see 63A). **Fl:** July-August. **I:** Garðabrúða. (Valerian family). — **Hill Valerian** *Valeriana sambucifolia* is closely related to Common Valerian, but smaller, with short runners, the leaves with fewer pairs of leaflets. Possibly all natural valerians in Iceland belong to this species; the separation of the two species appears rather vague.

Leaf (r. 0.4)

64 Mudwort
Limosella aquatica

Small plant with many, rather long-stalked (5-15 mm) flowers rising directly from base. Corolla five-parted, 3 mm wide, bell-shaped with v-shaped lobes, pink or nearly white. Sepals connected, green. Stamens four. One pistil, maturing to ovoid or nearly spherical capsule, 2-3 mm long. Tiny style remains attached after maturation. Many leaves in basal rosette, each on 2-4 cm long petiole; the blade lanceolate to elliptic, 5-12 mm long and 2-5 mm broad. Entire plant glabrous. **H:** 1-4 cm, usually growing close to the ground. **Hab:** Mud at the bottom of shallow ponds or bordering lakes, often in periodically inundated marshland. Here and there in the lowland. **Sim:** Easily recognized in flower; the leaves resemble some leaves of Creeping Speerwort (167), which differs, however, from Mudwort by the curved, rooting runners. **Fl:** July-August. **I:** Efjugras. (Figwort family).

Leaf
(m. 2.5)

65 Sea-milkwort
Glaux maritima

Small plant with procumbent stems and ascending branches. Flowers single in leaf axils, 5-parted. Perianth simple, white to red-spotted; perianth leaves united at the base, deeply incised, with rounded lobes. Stamens five, with reddish pink filaments. Bottle-shaped, single-styled pistil. Stem densely set with leaves, glabrous. Leaves opposite, obovate or elliptic, dark green, 6-12 mm long, 2-4 mm broad, glabrous. **H:** 3-8 cm. **Hab:** Saltmarshes and flooded, sandy soil on the beach. Very rare. **Sim:** None. **Fl:** July-August. **I:** Sandlæðingur. (Primrose family).

Fruit
(m. 5)

66 Amphibious Bistort
Persicaria amphibia

Tall, glabrous, aquatic plant. Many-flowered spike on top of stems; corolla five-parted, petals reddish pink, obtuse. Stamens five, pistil with two styles connected at the base. Leaves narrowly ovate to lanceolate, alternate, 4-13 cm long and 1.5-3 cm broad, greyish green or tinged with red, long-stalked with basal sheath; blade with distinct midrib and regular lateral veins. **H:** 20-60 cm. **Hab:** Lakes or large ponds. Very rare. **Sim:** Easily recognized in flower, the leaves resemble Pondweed (197-203), but differ in the distinctly pinnate veins, usually with obtuse to truncate base. All pondweeds have parallel-veined leaves. **Fl:** July. **I:** Tjarnablaðka. (Dock family). — **Redshank** *Persicaria maculata* is related to Amphibious Bistort, but is a non-aquatic alien. The leaves are lanceolate, acute, tapering down to a short petiole. The leaf sheaths are ciliate, membranous. The flowers are reddish pink, in many-flowered raceme at the end of stem. Occurs in several localities in thermal soil, near hot springs and warm streams, and as a weed around greenhouses.

Fruit (m. 10)

67 Glaucous Dog-rose
Rosa dumalis

Flowers pink, 4-6 cm across, petals obcordate, 2-3 cm long. Sepals 1.5 cm long, acute, recurved. Leaves odd-pinnate, leaflets in two or three pairs, sharply dentate, ovate or elliptic, usually pointed, 2-3.5 cm long and 1.5-2.5 cm broad; stipules long, connected to petiole 1-1.5 cm up. Stem has distant, strong, claw-shaped thorns, the branches drooping. **H:** 50-150 cm. **Hab:** Woodland and fertile slopes. Very rare. **Sim:** Burnet Rose (77). The Glaucous Dog-rose differs through pink flowers, more distant thorns, larger stipules and sharper-toothed leaves. **Fl:** Has not been found flowering in natural habitats in Iceland, but blooms in gardens. **I:** Glitrós. (Rose family).

Twig with spines (m. 2)

68 Bilberry
Vaccinium myrtillus

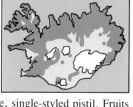

Flowers 6-8 mm across, 5-parted. Corolla reddish-green or pinkish-red, globose with narrow opening surrounded by five small, recurved lobes. Calyx disc-shaped, entire, violet. Stamens ten, anthers orange, with two hooks. One, single-styled pistil. Fruits about 1 cm in diameter, dark blue to blackish, or lighter blue when covered with thin vaxy bloom which is easily wiped off. Stem branches green, sharply angular or winged. Leaves alternate, ovate and finely denticulate, 10-20 mm long and 7-12 mm broad. **H:** Stems and branches ascending to about 10-20 cm. **Hab:** Depressions in slopes, heathland and woodland, mainly in snow-rich districts. Common in locations where snow cover is ensured throughout winter. In less snowy districts the bilberry will not be found in the lowland, but usually in snowbeds higher up in the mountain slopes. **Sim:** Bog Bilberry (69). The Bilberry can be recognized by the green, sharply angular branches, by toothed leaves, and shape of the flower. **Fl:** June. **I:** Aðalbláberjalyng. (Heath family).

Leaf
(m. 1.9)

69 Bog Bilberry
Vaccinium uliginosum

Flowers 5-parted. Corolla barrel- or bell-shaped, slightly incised, white, pink or red, often particoloured, 4 mm broad and 5 mm long. Calyx small, green or bluish with red, appressed lobes. Stamens ten, anthers with two filiform, upswept hooks. One, single-styled pistil. Fruit blue, often with greyish bloom, 9-12 mm wide. Branches round, brown, with alternate leaves. Leaves obovate, obtuse, or slightly pointed, 10-18 mm long and 6-12 mm broad, entire, reticulate-veined, with slightly recurved margin. **H:** Stems ascending 8-15 cm. **Hab:** Heathland, depressions and slopes, sometimes on hummocks in bogs. Common. **Sim:** Bilberry (68). The Bog Bilberry differs in the round, brown branches, and entire, obtuse leaves. Bog Rosemary (see 148B). **Fl:** May-June. **I:** Bláberjalyng. (Heath family).

Leaf
(m. 2.3)

70 Alpine Fleabane
Erigeron borealis

Stem usually unbranched, terminating in single, 1-1.5 cm broad flower head; sometimes branched with flower head on each branch. Flower heads covered with numerous, lanceolate bracts below. Bracts red-tipped, grey-haired, for the most part appressed. White or pinkish-violet, ligulate rayflorets form a circle around the yellow, tubular discflorets in centre of flower head. Each discfloret surrounded by hairs (pappus), that are often slightly longer than the flower tubes themselves. Stem hairy, with lanceolate, pointed, stalkless leaves; the basal leaves oblong and obtuse, but short-pointed. **H:** 10-25 cm. **Hab:** Grassy heathland and slopes. Common. **Sim:** Dwarf Fleabane (see 72). **Fl:** June. **I:** Jakobsfífill. (Daisy family).

Leaves (m. 0.9)

71 Snow Fleabane
Erigeron humilis

Small mountain plant with one to three stems from same base, each tipped with 1.5 cm wide flower head. Bottom of head more tapering towards stem than on other fleabanes. Involucral bracts bright violet with violet hairs. Rayflorets have white, ligulate corolla. Discflorets yellowish. Stem with spotted, white and violet hairs. Leaves oblong to lanceolate, the lowest ones spatulate, tapering to the petiole. **H:** 2-6 cm. **Hab:** Grassy brinks and slopes at high altitudes. Rare. **Sim:** Dwarf Fleabane (72). The Snow Fleabane differs in the violet hairs (instead of white) on the bracts, and funnel-shaped bottom of the head. **Fl:** June-July. **I:** Snækobbi. (Daisy family). — The Snow Fleabane prefers the more continental climate in the N of the Central Highlands. It rarely occurs below 700 m.

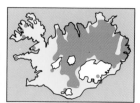

Flowerhead (m. 1.5)

72 Dwarf Fleabane
Erigeron uniflorus

Flowers form 1.5 cm wide heads. Rayflorets white or pink; discflorets yellow. Involucral bracts dark violet, esp. the tip, pointed, white-haired, the lowest ones more or less reflexed. Stem hairy, stem leaves lanceolate, some of the basal leaves spatulate or obovate on winged stalk. **H:** 4-10 cm. **Hab:** Mountain heaths and slopes. Rather common in upland mountains. **Sim:** Alpine Fleabane (70). Dwarf Fleabane is lower with relatively larger head, usually with some of the basal leaves spatulate and obtuse; it also has more reflexed involucral bracts. Snow Fleabane (71). The Dwarf Fleabane differs in the white bract hairs, and more truncate bottom of the head. **Fl:** June-July. **I:** Fjallakobbi. (Daisy family).

Flowerhead and leaves (1:1)

73 Glacier Buttercup
Ranunculus glacialis

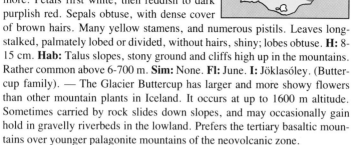

Flowers 2-2.5 cm wide, usually single on each stem. Corolla with five free petals, sometimes more. Petals first white, then reddish to dark purplish red. Sepals obtuse, with dense cover of brown hairs. Many yellow stamens, and numerous pistils. Leaves long-stalked, palmately lobed or divided, without hairs, shiny; lobes obtuse. **H:** 8-15 cm. **Hab:** Talus slopes, stony ground and cliffs high up in the mountains. Rather common above 6-700 m. **Sim:** None. **Fl:** June. **I:** Jöklasóley. (Buttercup family). — The Glacier Buttercup has larger and more showy flowers than other mountain plants in Iceland. It occurs at up to 1600 m altitude. Sometimes carried by rock slides down slopes, and may occasionally gain hold in gravelly riverbeds in the lowland. Prefers the tertiary basaltic mountains over younger palagonite mountains of the neovolcanic zone.

Leaf (1:1)

74 Sea Mayweed
Matricaria maritima

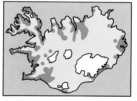

Large perennial with many flower heads about 3-5 cm wide. Rayflorets white, the ligulate corolla 3-5 mm broad and 1.5 cm long. Discflorets with tubular, yellow corolla on elevated receptacle. Involucral bracts oblong, green with dark brown to blackish membranous margin. Stem and branches furrowed. Leaves pinnate, with dissected leaflets and linear lobules. **H:** 20-60 cm. **Hab:** Dumps, waste places and industrial fields, also along the coast. Common in towns and villages. **Sim:** Oxeye Daisy (75) has the same type of flower heads, but different leaves which are pinnately lobed or dentate but not divided. Pineappleweed (189) has similar leaves, but differs in lack of white rayflowers in the heads. **Fl:** July. **I:** Baldursbrá. (Daisy family).

Leaf (r. 0.5)

75 Oxeye Daisy
Leucanthemum vulgare

Large perennial with single, 4-5 cm wide flower head on top of stem. Rayflorets white. Ligulate corolla 3-5 mm broad, 1.5-2.5 cm long. Discflorets yellow. Involucral bracts oblong, green, bordered by dark brown to blackish membrane. Stem furrowed. Leaves ligulate to spatulate, not divided but lobed or coarsely dentate, short-haired or glabrous; basal leaves tapering to narrow petiole, upper leaves sessile, clasping the stem. **H:** 30-60 cm. **Hab:** Unstable alien in seeded grasslands and gardens. Rare. **Sim:** Sea Mayweed (see 74). **Fl:** July. **I:** Freyjubrá. (Daisy family).

Leaves (r. 0.7)

76 Mountain Avens
Dryas octopetala

Large flowers, 2.5-3.5 cm wide. Petals white, usually eight but sometimes more. Stamens numerous, yellow, clustered in centre of flower. Many pistils, the style growing into a long, pinnately haired beak when the fruit matures. Leaves on prostrate, woody shoots, 1.2-2.2 cm long, ovate, dentate with blunt teeth, on short petiole, shiny and very thin-haired on upper side, with dense, white cover of woollen hairs on lower side. Leaf margin revolute. **H:** 5-10 cm. **Hab:** Gravelly hills and dry heathland. Common. **Sim:** None. **Fl:** May-June. **I:** Holtasóley. (Rose family). — This plant has three different names in Icelandic depending on maturity. The name "holtasóley" (heath buttercup) is used at flowering time and "hárbrúða" (hairy doll) after the fruit has matured (right). The leafy shoots, found in all seasons, are called "rjúpnalauf" (ptarmigan leaves).

Leaf (m. 1.6)

77 Burnet Rose
Rosa pimpinellifolia

Flowers 3-5 cm wide. Petals white, 1.5-2 cm long. Sepal lobes narrow, pointed, often toothed, 1-1.5 cm long. Stamens numerous, yellow. Several hairy pistils in centre of flower. The fruit, known as a "hip", resembles an almost spherical jar, dark reddish blue to almost black, 7-8 mm wide, hollow, with small nutlets inside. Leaves pinnate, usually with three to four leaflet pairs besides terminal leaflet. Leaflets elliptic, dentate, 1-2 cm long. Stem densely covered with small prickles and sparse larger thorns in between, 1-8 mm long. **H:** 30-70 cm. **Hab:** Grassy and shrubby slopes. Very rare. **Sim:** Glaucous Dog-rose (67). The Burnet Rose differs in its white flowers, its dense, differently sized prickles, and smaller stipules. **Fl:** July. **I:** Þyrnirós. (Rose family).

Twig with spines (m. 2.5)

78 Grass of Parnassus
Parnassia palustris

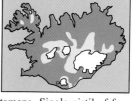

Flowers 1.5-2 cm wide, single on top of stem.
Petals white with darker veins, obtuse. Sepals
only half the length of petals. Stamens five with
white anthers. Five branched, greenish yellow
and nectar-bearing staminodes alternate with stamens. Single pistil of four
carpels. Stem glabrous, with a single leaf; the basal leaves ovate to cordate,
entire, glabrous, the petiole longer than the blade. **H:** 8-15 cm. **Hab:** In short-
grown grassland, grassy heaths, moist ground and sometimes in open soil.
Common. **Sim:** None. **Fl:** June-July. **I:** Mýrasóley. (Parnassus-grass family).
— The traditional Icelandic name "mýrasóley" (bog buttercup) is hardly ap-
propriate as it usually grows in moderately dry soil rather than in bogs. It is not
part of the buttercup family, but related to the Saxifrages.

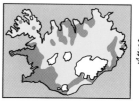

Flower (m. 1.4)

79 Wild Strawberry
Fragaria vesca

Flowers 1.2-1.5 cm wide, 5-parted. Petals
white, obovate. Sepals shorter, pointed;
epicalyx lobes shorter and narrower than the
sepals. Stamens ten. Many pistils, developing
into small, dark nutlets on the surface of the "strawberry" which is formed by
the expanded receptacle. Rather stout rhizome with ascending, trifoliolate
leaves on long, hairy petiole. Leaflets rhomboid or obovate, coarsely toothed,
with silvery hairs on lower side, 1.5-3 cm long and 1-2 cm broad. **H:** 5-15 cm,
prostrate runners much longer. **Hab:** South-facing slopes or woodland here
and there throughout the country, preferring the warmer districts. **Sim:** The
flowers resemble Parnassus-grass (78), but the wild strawberries differ in the
three-fingered leaves. When not in flower the Strawberry may be mistaken for
Stone Bramble (116); the strawberry leaves differ in unstalked terminal leaflet, denser hair cover on underside and petiole. **Fl:** July. **I:** Jarðarber. (Rose
family). — The wild strawberries mature late and are usually rather small in
Iceland. Where favourable conditions are found in fertile, sunny slopes, they
ripen fully and are used for human consumption; they are tastier than the
larger, cultivated strawberries.

Leaf (r. 0.7)

80 Dwarf Cornel
Cornus suecica

At first sight the dwarf cornel appears to have single, rather large (1.5-2.5 cm), white, four-parted flowers with unequal-sized pairs of opposite petals. In reality these large petals are transformed, white foliage leaves lacking chlorophyll, almost indiscernibly red-tipped, surrounding 6-20 tiny, short-stalked, purplish black flowers in terminal corymb on the stem. The actual perianth is only 1-2 mm wide, the sepals fused to bell-shaped calyx with 4 V-shaped lobes. Petals purplish black with four reflexed lobes. Stamens four with yellowish white anthers. Single, dark-styled pistil extending out of the flower, developing into a rather large, red drupe at maturity. Pedicels have white, appressed hairs. Leaves opposite, elliptic or ovate, 1.5-2.5 cm long, pointed, with curved, parallel veins, like the large, white bracts. **H:** Upright shoots 8-20 cm, arising from horizontal rhizome with membranous scale leaves. **Hab:** Dwarf-shrub heaths and slopes, usually forming large, continuous cover. Rare. **Sim:** None. **Fl:** July. **I:** Skollaber. (Dogwood family).

Individual flower (m. 10)

81 Sea Campion
Silene uniflora

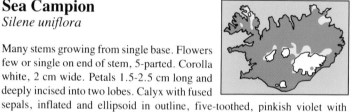

Many stems growing from single base. Flowers few or single on end of stem, 5-parted. Corolla white, 2 cm wide. Petals 1.5-2.5 cm long and deeply incised into two lobes. Calyx with fused sepals, inflated and ellipsoid in outline, five-toothed, pinkish violet with darker net of veins, 1.5 cm long. Stamens ten with oblong, dark anthers. One pistil with four to six styles. Leaves opposite, entire, glabrous, lanceolate or narrow-elliptical, 1-2 cm long. **H:** Stems 10-25 cm long, usually more or less decumbent. **Hab:** Gravel and sandy soil. Common where gravelly soil is present, esp. in the deserts of the Central Highlands. **Sim:** Easily recognized by the inflated calyx. **Fl:** June. **I:** Holurt. (Pink family). — The Sea Campion is known in Iceland by many different names. Children sometimes call it "Fly flower" because small flies get trapped within the inflated calyx. This often leads to the erroneous conclusion that the plant is carnivorous.

Calyx (m. 1.7)

82 Alpine Mouse-ear
Cerastium alpinum

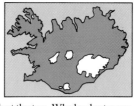

Flowers 1.5-2 cm wide. Petals five, white, bilobed. Sepals half or 2/3 the length of the petals, 6-8 mm, acute, glandular, with membranous margin. Stamens ten, one 5-styled pistil. Fruit is a capsule, opening into ten marginal teeth at the top. Whole plant more or less grey due to woollen hairs. Stem with opposite, 0.6-1.8 cm long and 3-6 mm broad leaves; the leaves elliptic to lanceolate, sessile. **H:** 8-18 cm. **Hab:** Gravelly soil, heathland and dry slopes. Common. **Sim:** Common Mouse-ear (98). The Alpine Mouse-ear differs in larger flowers, the petals distinctly longer than the sepals. Arctic Mouse-ear (see 83). **Fl:** May-June. **I:** Músareyra. (Pink family). — **Smooth Mouse-ear** *Cerastium glabratum* is a nearly glabrous variety except at the leaf base, with delicate, dark, slender pedicels.

Fruit in calyx (m. 2.5)

83 Arctic Mouse-ear
Cerastium arcticum

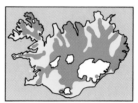

Flowers 1-1.5 cm wide. Petals five, white, bilobed. Sepals half or 2/3 the length of the petals, 6-8 mm long, acute, glandular, with membranous margin. Stamens ten, one 5-styled pistil. Fruit is a 10-toothed capsule. Stem bears glandular hairs and opposite, 0.8-1.5 cm long and 4-8 mm broad leaves. Leaves obovate or elliptic, unstalked, hairy, esp. on margin. **H:** 5-15 cm. **Hab:** Gravelly soil in mountains. Common above 600 m. **Sim:** Alpine Mouse-ear (82). The Arctic Mouse-ear is brighter green, less tomentose, the bottom of the calyx broader and more rounded, the fruit shorter and broader. These two species are not easily identified, but it should be kept in mind, that the Arctic Mouse-ear is restricted to high altitudes. The Alpine Mouse-ear is found equally at high altitudes as in the lowland. **Fl:** June-July. **I:** Fjallafræhyrna. (Pink family).

Fruit in calyx (m. 2.5)

84 Starwort Mouse-ear
Cerastium cerastoides

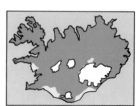

Flowers 7-10 mm wide. Petals white, 7-8 mm long, bilobed. Sepals 5 mm long, with membranous margin. Stamens ten, anthers yellow. One pistil with three to four, rarely five styles. Stem and calyx covered with glandular hairs. Leaves opposite, glabrous, oblong to lanceolate, blunt; the leaf pairs usually both curved towards the same side. **H:** 3-6 cm, the stems usually decumbent. **Hab:** In moist soil, along small creeks, in mossy, cold springs. Common at higher altitudes. **Sim:** Differs from Alpine Mouse-ear (82) and Common Mouse-ear (98) in the sideways-curved, glabrous leaf pairs, and fewer styles. **Fl:** June. **I:** Lækjafræhyrna. (Pink family).

Leafy shoot (m. 1.2)

85 Chickweed Wintergreen
Trientalis europaea

Flowers 1-1.8 cm wide, usually single, sometimes two or three on slender pedicels. Petals usually seven, white or slightly pinkish, acute, with yellow spot at the base. Sepals lanceolate, acute, 4-5 mm long. Stamens usually seven with yellow anthers. Single pistil with one, long style. Leaves 5-7 in a rosette on upper part of stem, broad-lanceolate to obovate, almost without petiole, thin, glabrous, 2-3 cm long and 8-13 mm broad; only quite small leaves on lower part of stem. **H:** 6-12 cm. **Hab:** As an undergrowth in heaths and woodland. Rather common in the East. **Sim:** None. Easily recognized by leaves being in top-rosette, and by 7-parted flower. **Fl:** July. **I:** Sjöstjarna. (Primerose family). — **Wood-sorrel** *Oxalis acetosella* is a very rare species with 5-parted, white flowers and darker veins, 1.5-2 cm wide. Stamens ten, one pistil. Seeds are violently discharged from mature fruit. Leaves are long-petioled, trifoliolate, reminiscent of clover, but differ through obcordate leaflets. The rhizome set with small, thick scale leaves. (Wood-sorrel family).

Leaf
(r. 0.8)

86 Bogbean
Menyanthes trifoliata

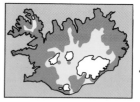

Flowers stalked in short raceme on top of stem, 2-3 cm wide, 5-parted. Flowerbuds red before opening. Corolla white, split half way down or more into five lobes; the petal lobes tipped with reddish tint, set with white appendages on the inside. Calyx rather deeply cleft, the segments blunt, reddish green. Stamens five, anthers dark. One, single-styled pistil with three-parted stigma. Leaves trifoliolate on 10-30 cm long stalk, the leaflets 4-10 cm long and 2-6 cm broad, glabrous, obovate or broad-elliptic, entire. Rhizome long and jointed, about 7-10 mm thick. **H:** 20-30 cm or more if growing in water. **Hab:** Bogs, ditches and pond margins. Rather common. **Sim:** None. **Fl:** June. **I:** Horblaðka. (Bogbean family). — The Bogbean has a very strong rhizome, which was formerly used in Iceland in making packsaddles for horses. It flowers and is quite vigorous when growing in water, but carries relatively small leaves, and rarely flowers where the ground-water level is below the surface.

Flower
(m. 1.2)

87 Mossy Saxifrage
Saxifraga hypnoides

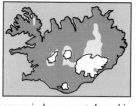

Flowers are few or single on each stem, 1.5-2 cm wide. Petals white with darker veins, obovate. Sepals about 1/3 the length of petals. Stamens ten. Top of pistil cleft into two segments with two styles. Basal leaves about 1 cm long, narrow in lower part, broad in front with 3-5, rarely 7, pointed teeth; Stem- and shoot-leaves usually entire, nearly linear, alternate. **H:** 10-15 cm. **Hab:** Rocky slopes and slides, ravines. Rather common. **Sim:** Tufted Saxifrage (89). The Mossy Saxifrage differs in the long, thin-leaved shoots, it is also slightly bigger with larger flowers. **Fl:** June. **I:** Mosasteinbrjótur. (Saxifrage family).

Leafy shoots (r. 0.6)

88 Drooping Saxifrage
Saxifraga cernua

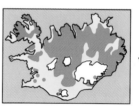

Flowers 10-18 mm wide. Petals white. Sepals about 1/3 the length of petals. Stamens ten; the top of pistil two-cleft with two styles. Leaves reniform, with five (seven) broad, V-shaped lobes at the front; the uppermost stem-leaves trifid or entire. Small dark red bulbils in upper leaf axils. White, thick-leaved bulbils at the base. **H:** 8-20 cm. **Hab:** Ravines, cliffs and upper slopes of mountains. Rather common in some areas, esp. in the North. **Sim:** The flowers resemble Mossy Saxifrage (87) but the leaves resemble Brook Saxifrage (96). The Drooping Saxifrage is best recognized by the red bulbils in the leaf axils. **Fl:** June-July. **I:** Laukasteinbrjótur. (Saxifrage family). — **Meadow Saxifrage** *Saxifraga granulata* is a rare alien, resembling Drooping Saxifrage; it has bulbils at the base, the leaves are more rounded and less incised.

Leaf (m. 1.6)

89 Tufted Saxifrage
Saxifraga caespitosa

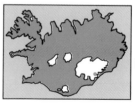

Flowers are 8-15 mm wide. Petals white to creamy, about double the length of sepals. Stamens ten, top of pistil two-cleft with two styles. Leaves with narrow base, broader, and with 3-5 pointed teeth at the front, in compact, small rosettes on short, usually densely clustered shoots. Stem covered with short glands. **H:** 5-15 cm. **Hab:** Gravelly hills, cliffs and rock outcrops. Common. **Sim:** Mossy Saxifrage (see 87). **Fl:** May-June. **I:** Þúfusteinbrjótur. (Saxifrage family). — Tufted Saxifrage is often divided into two subspecies, ssp. *caespitosa* and ssp. *decipiens*, which are often treated as separate species (*Saxifraga rosacea*). Ssp. *decipiens* has thinner, less compact clusters of leaf shoots, and large flowers with relatively longer petals, usually more than double the length of the sepals.

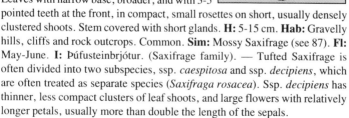

Leaf (m. 5)

90 Starry Saxifrage
Saxifraga stellaris

Flowers 1-1.4 cm wide, star-shaped. Petals elliptic to broad-lanceolate, white with two yellow spots on the inner side at the base. Sepals 3-4 mm long, red-tipped underneath. Stamens ten, anthers reddish yellow. Pistil with bifid top, light greenish yellow or red. Stem leafless, sparsely hairy. Leaves basal, 1.5-2.5 cm long, pointed and coarsely dentate at the front, thin-haired. **H:** 3-15 cm. **Hab:** Mossy springs, brook-beds, moist soil. Common. **Sim:** Foliolose Saxifrage (see 90A). **Fl:** June-July. **I:** Stjörnusteinbrjótur. (Saxifrage family). — Starry Saxifrage is typically found near cold mountain springs in light green Fountain Moss, in the company of Chickweed Willowherb (45) and Starwort Mouse-ear (84). — **Foliolose Saxifrage** *Saxifraga foliolosa* is related to Starry Saxifrage, but is rare and only found at high altitudes. It does not usually bloom, but carries clusters of dark reddish brown, reproductive bulbils at the end of pedicels. The leaves resemble Starry Saxifrage, but narrower.

*Leaf
(m. 1.8)*

91 Lesser Stitchwort
Stellaria graminea

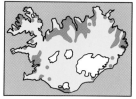

Flowers 10-14 mm wide. Five white petals, split almost to the base, thus appearing as ten. Sepals three-veined with broad membranous margin. Stamens ten with reddish brown anthers. Pistil three- or four-styled. Bracts membranous, with ciliate margin towards the base. Stems slender, four-angled, repeatedly branched, with opposite, sessile leaves; the leaves lanceolate, broader towards the base, tapering to a narrow point, 15-20 mm long. **H:** 20-50 cm. **Hab:** Homefields, roadsides and grassy roadside ditches. Introduced but widely established on farms and in villages. **Sim:** Fleshy Stitchwort (109). The Lesser Stitchwort differs in the membranous, ciliate bracts, larger flowers and longer leaves with broader base. **Fl:** June-July. **I:** Akurarfi. (Pink family). — The Lesser Stitchwort is one of the more recent aliens in Iceland, but has spread exceptionally fast through the Icelandic countryside the last few decades.

*Leaf
(m. 2.5)*

92 Thread-leaved Water-crowfoot
Ranunculus trichophyllus

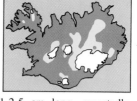

Aquatic plant growing under water, but flowering on the surface. Flowers 8-12 mm wide. Petals five, white, with yellowish base, 7-8 mm long. Sepals 3-4 mm. Stamens numerous. Pistils 10-20, single-styled. Leaves alternate, 1-2.5 cm long, repeatedly branched, with filiform lobes; membranous sheath at the leaf base. Entire plant glabrous except for pistils and leaf base. **H:** 15-35 cm. **Hab:** Shallow pools, ponds and ditches. Common. **Sim:** None. Easily recognized by the white, floating flowers, and the finely dissected, submerged leaves. **Fl:** July-August. **I:** Lónasóley. (Buttercup family). — The Thread-leaved Watercrowfoot, together with the Slender-leaved Pondweed (202), is frequently among the first aquatic settlers in newly formed roadside pools and ditches, and sometimes the only aquatic plant in pools in the glacier moraines of the Central Highlands.

Leaf
(m. 1.3)

93 Diapensia
Diapensia lapponica

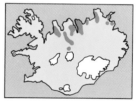

Flowers 10-12 mm wide. Petals white. Sepals blunt, greenish yellow or tinted with red, bordered by narrow membrane. Stamens five, pistil of three carpels, with one long style. Leaves entire, oblong to spatulate, 5-10 mm, evergreen, rather thick and stiff, glabrous with revolute margin, forming continous, dense cushions consisting of compact leaf rosettes on many, flowerless shoots. **H:** 2-8 cm. **Hab:** Hilltops, mountain flats, usually on rather moist heath-soil. Rather rare, found only in the North. **Sim:** Non-flowering shoots resemble Trailing Azalea (55). The flowers resemble those of Tufted Saxifrage (89), but here the Diapensia can be identified by the leaves. **Fl:** June. **I:** Fjallabrúða. (Diapensia family). — The Diapensia has a rather peculiar distribution in the northern coastal mountains. It was only recently discovered also in the uplands of Skagafjörður, and one locality in the NW of Iceland.

Fruit in open calyx
(m. 3.3)

94 Pyramidal Saxifrage
Saxifraga cotyledon

Repeatedly branched herb with numerous flowers; flower clusters rising from every leaf axil in upper part of stem. Flowers 1.2-1.8 cm wide. Petals spatulate, ciliate in basal part, white, frequently red-veined. Sepals 4-5 mm long, with short, red glandular hairs. Stamens ten, top of pistil two-cleft with two styles. Leaves form dense, regular basal rosette, obovate or ligulate, thick, 10-15 mm broad, evergreen, minutely denticulate with white-crusted teeth. **H:** 10-40 cm. **Hab:** Vertical cliffs and rock faces. Widespread in the East from Skaftártunga northwards to Seyðisfjörður. **Sim:** Silver Saxifrage (95) has similar but smaller leaf-rosette, but inflorescence is much less branched with fewer and smaller flowers. **Fl:** July. **I:** Klettafrú. (Saxifrage family).

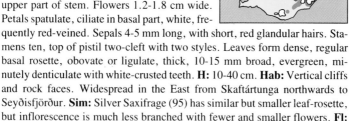

Leaf
(r. 0.9)

95 Silver Saxifrage
Saxifraga paniculata

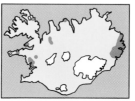

Several white, 5-parted, 1 cm wide flowers in short raceme on top of stem. Petals with blunt end, calyx short. Stamens ten, one bifid pistil. Stem glandular with alternate, ca. 5 mm long leaves. Basal leaves in rosette, ligulate, 7-15 mm long and 5 mm broad; the leaf margin with tiny, white-crusted teeth. **H:** 10-18 cm. **Hab:** Fissures in rock faces, gorge walls and cliffsides. Rare. **Sim:** Pyramidal Saxifrage (94). The Silver Saxifrage has a much less branched inflorescence, and smaller, esp. narrower leaves in the rosette. **Fl:** July. **I:** Bergsteinbrjótur. (Saxifrage family).

Leaf
(m. 2.5)

96 Alpine Brook Saxifrage
Saxifraga rivularis

Flowers 7-10 mm wide. Petals white, rarely with slight pinkish tint. Sepals obtuse. Stamens ten, the pistil divided in upper part, two-styled. Leaves long-petioled, short and broad, usually five-lobed, some three-lobed; the lobes blunt. **H:** 3-12 cm. **Hab:** Along creeks, springs and in moist cliffsides, most frequent at higher altitudes. Common. **Sim:** Drooping Saxifrage (88). The Brook Saxifrage differs in lacking red bulbils in leaf axils, and smaller flowers; the leaves are similar. **Fl:** June-July. **I:** Lækjasteinbrjótur. (Saxifrage family). — A small, reddish mountain variety of Brook Saxifrage, called **Arctic Brook Saxifrage** *Saxifraga hyperborea* is sometimes regarded as separate species. It is rather rare in Iceland, usually found above 900 m.

Leaf
(m. 1.6)

97 Alpine Snow Saxifrage
Saxifraga nivalis

Many flowers clustered at top of stem, 5-parted, 5-6 mm across, white, sometimes with greenish or pinkish tint. Calyx split half way down, green or red. Stamens ten, pistil with two-cleft top, two-styled. Stem tomentose, leafless below the inflorescence. Basal leaves with short, winged stalk, the blade nearly round, 1-2 cm wide, with coarse, blunt teeth. **H:** 8-16 cm. **Hab:** Cliffs and gorges in the lowland, common in the mountains. **Sim:** Slender Snow Saxifrage (see 97A). **Fl:** June-July. **I:** Snæsteinbrjótur. (Saxifrage family). — **Slender Snow Saxifrage** *Saxifraga tenuis* is closely related to Alpine Snow Saxifrage, but much smaller, usually 2-5 cm. The basal leaves are usually sessile, 5-7 mm broad. The stigmas are on hooked styles with the tip bent down. Occurs only at high altitudes. Closely related species, not always clearly separated.

Leaf
(m. 1.4)

98 Common Mouse-ear
Cerastium fontanum

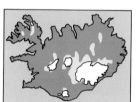

Flowers 5-8 mm wide. Petals white, bilobed, about the same length as the sepals, which are acute, hairy, with membranous margin. Stamens ten, pistil single, usually 5-styled. Fruit is a capsule with ten teeth. Leaves opposite, ovate-oblong, with blunt end, 10-20 mm long. **H:** 10-30 cm. **Hab:** Heathland, open soil, roadsides and homefields. Common. **Sim:** Alpine Mouse-ear (82). The Common Mouse-ear differs in being less hairy; the petals slightly or not longer than sepals. **Fl:** May-June. **I:** Vegarfi. (Pink family). — **Sticky Mouse-ear** *Cerastium glomeratum* is a rather rare, annual plant; resembles Common Mouse-ear and Alpine Mouse-ear. The flowers are usually more numerous in denser cymes, petals usually of same length or little longer than sepals, the fruits shiny with golden-yellow tint, the leaves broader, ovate to elliptic, apiculate. Occurs only in S and SW Iceland.

Open fruit in calyx
(m. 3)

99 Corn Spurrey
Spergula arvensis

Flowers 5-parted, 4-6 mm wide. Petals white, slightly longer than the sepals, blunt. Sepals green or red-tinted, with narrow marginal membrane. Stamens five or ten. One 5-styled pistil; the fruit splits into five lobes at maturity. Stems glandular. Leaves filiform, 1-4 cm long, usually 6-8 or more in whorls on the stem. **H:** 5-25 cm. **Hab:** Open, moderately moist soil, waste places, roadsides. Widespread throughout southern part of country, rare elsewhere. **Sim:** Lesser Spurrey (see 99A). **Fl:** July. **I:** Skurfa. (Pink family). — **Lesser Spurrey** *Spergularia marina* is a very rare species resembling Corn Spurrey, but more delicate with three-styled pistil. Occurs only on beaches and mud-flats along the seashore.

Open fruit in calyx
(m. 3.4)

100 Arctic Sandwort
■
☐
Arenaria norvegica

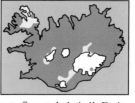

Small, branched plant with decumbent, very
short-haired branches. Flowers 6-9 mm across.
Petals white, obtuse, longer than the sepals
which are acute, three- to five-veined with nar-
row marginal membrane. Stamens ten, one three- to five-styled pistil. Fruits
ovoid to nearly spherical capsules, usually with six teeth. Leaves opposite, elliptic or broadly lanceolate, shiny, 2-5 mm long. **H:** 3-10 cm, usually decumbent. **Hab:** Open soil or sand, waste ground or gravel hills. Common. **Sim:**
Pearlwort, esp. Knotted Pearlwort (106), and Sandwort (102-104). The Arctic Sandwort differs in having 6-toothed capsule (3 on other sandworts and
usually 4-5 on pearlworts) and in broader, elliptic and shiny leaves. **Fl:** June.
I: Skeggsandi. (Pink family).

Open fruit in calyx
(m. 3.5)

101 Sea Sandwort
☐
■
Honckenya peploides

Flowers five-parted, 8-15 mm wide. Petals
white, obcordate to spatulate, with narrow
claw; sepals of similar length or longer, green,
ovate, acute. Stamens ten, single pistil with
three (four) styles. Fruit is a rather large, spherical, green capsule, resembling
a berry. All flowers of the same plant usually have either sterile stamens or
sterile pistils, therefore functionally unisexual. Stem with two, longitudinal
furrows, nearly four-sided, glabrous. Leaves glabrous as well, thick and
fleshy, elliptic, ovate or obovate, entire, sessile, opposite, 1-2.5 cm long and
5-15 mm broad. **H:** 15-20 cm, usually with repeatedly branched underground
stems, whereby a single plant can cover an area of several sq. feet. **Hab:** Sand
beaches. Common all around the country where sandy shores are found.
Where sand extends inland from the shores, the plant may occasionally be
found a few miles away from the shore, though generally restricted to the
seashore. **Sim:** Easily distinguished by the thick, fleshy, green or yellowish-
green leaves, and by the habitat. **Fl:** June. **I:** Fjöruarfi. (Pink family).

Fruit in calyx
(m. 4)

102 Mountain Sandwort
Minuartia rubella

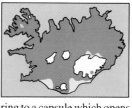

Small plant with 4-6 mm wide flowers, pedicels usually hairy, but occasionally glabrous. Petals white, somewhat shorter than the sepals which are pointed, with three raised veins. Stamens ten. One three-styled pistil, maturing to a capsule which opens terminally into three teeth. Leaves narrowly lanceolate to linear, opposite, clearly three-veined. **H:** 3-6 cm. **Hab:** Gravelly hills, sandy soil, bare ground or screes. Common. **Sim:** Alpine Pearlwort (105). The Mountain Sandwort differs in the narrow-pointed, three-veined, usually brown or reddish brown rather than green sepals. Teesdale Sandwort (103). The Mountain Sandwort differs in the relative short, slightly hairy pedicels, the sepals with sharper, straighter point than Teesdale Sandwort. **Fl:** June-July. **I:** Melanóra. (Pink family).

Calyx (m. 7)

103 Teesdale Sandwort
Minuartia stricta

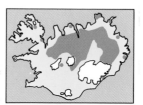

Whole plant more or less brownish violet. Flowers 4-5 mm across. Petals white, of same length or longer than sepals which are pointed, dark violet-brown. Stamens ten. Pistil three-styled, the fruit a capsule opening into three teeth. Leaves linear, opposite, more or less reddish brown to violet. **H:** 3-8 cm. **Hab:** Open soil in heathland. Rather rare except in the N and NE. **Sim:** Mountain Sandwort (102). The Teesdale Sandwort can by recognized by its less distinct veins and the sepals, whose point is not as sharp, and slightly curved. The uppermost internode of the stem below the flowers is usually many times the calyx length on Teesdale Sandwort, but only two or three times the calyx length on Mountain Sandwort. **Fl:** Juny-July. **I:** Móanóra. (Pink family).

Calyx (m. 7)

104 Two-flowered Sandwort
Minuartia biflora

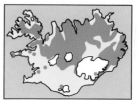

Small plant, the flowers 4-6 mm wide, pedicels always short-haired. Petals white, of similar length or longer than the sepals. Sepals blunt, green, three-veined. Stamens ten, pistil with three or four styles. Capsule splits terminally into three lobes at maturity. Leaves narrowly lanceolate to linear, opposite. **H:** 2-5 cm. **Hab:** Open soil and moist ground. Widespread to common at higher altitudes. **Sim:** Mountain Sandwort (102). The Two-flowered Sandwort differs in being entirely green, and having blunt sepals. Alpine Pearlwort (105). The Two-flowered Sandwort differs through larger flowers, longer sepals, and three styles rather than five. **Fl:** June. **I:** Fjallanóra. Pink family).

Calyx (m. 5.5)

105 Alpine Pearlwort
Sagina saginoides

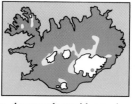

Delicate, light-green, glabrous plant. Flowers 4-5 mm wide, usually 5-parted, open only in sunshine. Petals white, equal in length to the sepals, which are obtuse with membranous margin. Stamens ten. Pistil with four to five styles, the capsule ovoid, opening into five lobes. Leaves opposite on the stem, and in basal rosette, linear, 4-10 mm long and less than 1 mm broad, sharp-pointed. **H:** 3-6 cm. **Hab:** Steep slopes, vertical banks, open soil. Common. **Sim:** Procumbent Pearlwort (193). The Alpine Pearlwort differs through 5-parted flowers, appressed calyx when in fruit, and longer pedicels. **Fl:** June. **I:** Langkrækill. (Pink family). — **Heath Pearlwort** *Sagina subulata* resembles Alpine Pearlwort, but the leaves have a much longer terminal point (1/2 mm), and the whole plant is more or less glandular (magnifier!). Found here and there on gravel slopes and cliffsides on the seashore.

Fruit in calyx (m. 5.2)

106 Knotted Pearlwort
Sagina nodosa

Flowers 5-parted, 7-8 mm wide. Petals white, elliptic, longer than the sepals which are elliptic, green. Stamens 10, one 5-styled pistil. Leaves opposite, linear, 2-7 mm long, sharp-pointed; the stem leaves shorter than the basal leaves, with knotted leaf shoots in the axils. **H:** 3-8 cm. **Hab:** Open soil and roadsides. Rather common. **Sim:** Arctic Sandwort (100). The Knotted Pearlwort differs through narrower leaves, and knotted leaf-shoots. **Fl:** June-July. **I:** Hnúskakrækill. (Pink family). — **Tufted Pearlwort** *Sagina caespitosa* is a rare, small plant with 5-parted flowers and short pedicels. Resembles Snow Pearlwort (140) but forms small, round tufts. Grows on mountain edges or hill-tops, preferably on moist, open soil.

Leafy shoot (m. 2)

107 Common Chickweed
Stellaria media

Annual plant with 5-parted flowers. Petals white, split almost to the base, thus appearing ten, usually shorter than the sepals which are green, ovate-lanceolate with membranous margin, 4-6 mm long. Stamens ten, one pistil with three-lobed stigma. Leaves opposite, broadly ovate, 5-30 mm long, soft and juicy, on ciliate pedicel or sessile. Stem with two longitudinal stripes of hairs. **H:** 5-20 cm. **Hab:** Fertilized soil, gardens. Widespread through animal droppings, often spreading along sheep paths. Common. **Sim:** Fleshy Stitchwort (109). The Common Chickweed differs in the short petals, and broad leaves. **Fl:** May-Nov. **I:** Haugarfi. (Pink family).

Leaf (m. 1.5)

108 Fairy Flax

Linum catharticum

Several flowers in dichasium on each stem, white, 5-parted. Petals 4 mm long. Sepals green, acute and sharp-keeled, 2.5-3 mm long, with marginal glands. Stamens five; one pistil with 5-lobed style. Fruit is a spherical capsule. Stem slender. Leaves opposite, 6-10 mm long, narrowly elliptic to lanceolate, glabrous, entire. **H:** 10-20 cm. **Hab:** Grassy hillsides and slopes. Common in a few areas, absent in others. **Sim:** None. **Fl:** July. **I:** Villilín. (Flax family).

Fruit in calyx (m. 8)

109 Fleshy Stitchwort
Stellaria crassifolia

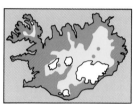

Flowers 7-10 mm wide, 5-parted. Petals split almost to the base, thus appearing ten. Sepals 3-4 mm long, acute, with membranous margin. Stamens ten, one three-styled pistil. Stems slender. Leaves opposite, elliptic or lanceolate, usually 6-12 mm long and 2-4 mm broad, or larger, nearly sessile, smooth, pointed. Thick-leaved reddish brown bulbils form on the tips of branches late in the fall. **H:** 15-30 cm. **Hab:** Moist grassland, lakesides or hummocks in bogs. Rather common, but escapes notice until late summer. **Sim:** Low Stitchwort (see 110). Northern Stitchwort (see 109A). Lesser Stitchwort (91). The Fleshy Stitchwort differs in narrower, tapering base of the leaves, in smaller flowers and green, nonciliate bracts. **Fl:** July. **I:** Stjörnuarfi. (Pink family). — **Northern Stitchwort** *Stellaria calycantha* is a rare species, much resembling Fleshy Stitchwort, but taller with smaller flowers, differing in having very short petals, much shorter than the sepals, and in the uppermost leaves having sparse marginal hairs (magnifier!) at the base.

Calyx (m. 8.5)

110 Low Stitchwort

Stellaria humifusa

Closely related to Fleshy Stitchwort, but restricted to salt marshes by the seashore. Flowers 8-12 mm wide. Petals split almost to the base, thus appearing ten. Sepals 3-4.5 mm, usually involute, blunt-tipped. Stamens ten, pistil three-styled. Stems glabrous with rather dense, opposite, elliptic, sessile, glabrous leaves. **H:** 3-8 cm. **Hab:** Short grown salt marshes. Widespread. **Sim:** Resembles Fleshy Stitchwort (109), but lower, more procumbent, with denser, thicker leaves, relatively larger flowers and blunt-tipped sepals. **Fl:** July. **I:** Lágarfi. (Pink family).

Calyx (m. 8)

108

111 Iceland-purslane
Koenigia islandica

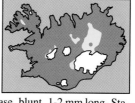

Annual plant. Several clustered flowers, usually more or less surrounded by the uppermost
leaves which are green or reddish. Perianth
simple, perianth leaves usually three, rarely
four, whitish, green or red, partly united at the base, blunt, 1-2 mm long. Stamens three, single pistil without style. Fruit is an ovoid, short-beaked, 2 mm
long nutlet. Stem usually red. Leaves obovate or nearly round, green or red,
entire, glabrous; membranous sheath at the base. **H:** 1-4 cm. **Hab:** Moist,
open soil, mud flats and periodically flooded creek-beds. Common. **Sim:**
None. **Fl:** June-July. **I:** Naflagras. (Dock family).

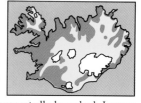

Fruit
(m. 20)

112 Alpine Bistort
Bistorta vivipara

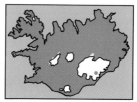

Flowers white, sometimes pinkish or greenish,
short-stalked in spike-like raceme on end of
stem. Perianth simple, 5-parted; perianth
leaves 3-4 mm long, obovate to pear-shaped.
Sepals lacking, but there are brownish, membranous bracts between the flowers. Stamens 6-8, anthers dark violet. Single, three-sided pistil with three
styles. Flowers in lower part of inflorescence usually replaced by brown,
greenish brown or red bulbils. Leaves stalked, the blade ovate to lanceolate,
2-6 cm long, 5-15 mm broad, dark green and shiny on top, light green with
prominent midrib underneath; leaf margin revolute. **H:** 8-20 cm. **Hab:** Very
diverse habitats, both dry and wet, from the shore up to about 1000 m in the
mountains. Very common. **Sim:** None. **Fl:** June-July. **I:** Kornsúra. (Dock
family).

Bulbil
(m. 8.5)

113 Knotgrass
Polygonum aviculare

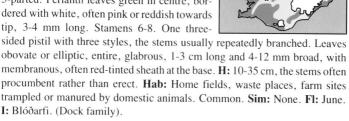

Several flowers in leaf axils. Perianth simple,
5-parted. Perianth leaves green in centre, bordered with white, often pink or reddish towards
tip, 3-4 mm long. Stamens 6-8. One three-
sided pistil with three styles, the stems usually repeatedly branched. Leaves
obovate or elliptic, entire, glabrous, 1-3 cm long and 4-12 mm broad, with
membranous, often red-tinted sheath at the base. **H:** 10-35 cm, the stems often
procumbent rather than erect. **Hab:** Home fields, waste places, farm sites
trampled or manured by domestic animals. Common. **Sim:** None. **Fl:** June.
I: Blóðarfi. (Dock family).

Flower
(m. 8.5)

114 Round-leaved Sundew
■□ *Drosera rotundifolia*
□□

Flowers few or solitary on end of stem, usually closed except in sunshine. Petals whitish, 3-4 mm long. Calyx split almost halfway down, greenish or dark-coloured, sepal lobes obtuse, often red-tipped. Flower stems leafless, red. Many round basal leaves, pinkish red to dark red, 3-4 mm wide on long petiole, with slimy, bright red, long (2-3 mm) glandular hairs. **H:** 2-5 cm. **Hab:** Mossy hummocks in acid bogs, boggy edges below hillsides. Rather rare. **Sim:** Easily recognized from all other plants by the glandular leaves. **Fl:** July. **I:** Sóldögg. (Sundew family).

Fruit in calyx
(m. 6)

115 Marsh Pennywort
□■ *Hydrocotyle vulgaris*
□□

Leaves round, star-veined, crenate, glabrous, 1-3 cm in diameter. Petioles 5-15 cm long, arising from prostrate rhizome, usually hairy just below the point of attachment to centre of leaf. Flowers tiny, in small, knob-shaped umbel, 5-parted; petals white, flowerbuds often pinkish. Pistil inferior, two-styled, made up of two carpels, the fruit a two-merous schizocarp. **H:** 5-15 cm. **Hab:** Restricted to thermal soil, growing around hot springs and warm streams. Rare. **Sim:** None. The Marsh Pennywort is the only species in Iceland with peltate, star-veined leaves. **Fl:** July-August. **I:** Vatnsnafli. (Parsley family).

Fruit
(m. 10)

116 Stone Bramble
□□ *Rubus saxatilis*
■■

Flowers 5-parted, 8-10 mm wide. Petals whitish, spatulate, with narrow claw. Calyx deeply cleft; sepals green, hairy, acute, 5-6 mm long. Leaves long-petioled, trifoliolate, the petioles hairy with small spines. Leaflets double serrate, ovate or rhomboid; the lateral leaflets sessile or nearly so, the terminal leaflet always with a short stalk; stipules small, 3-5 mm long. Fruits are red, glossy drupes grouped several together, 7-8 mm wide with one stone. **H:** Produces very long, prostrate stolons; upright branches usually only 10-20 cm. **Hab:** Grassy slopes and woodland. Rather common. **Sim:** Easily recognized in flower or in fruit; the leaves resemble those of Wild Strawberry (79). The leaves of the Stone Bramble differ in the stalk of the terminal leaflet, in the delicate spines on the leaf stalk, and in being less hairy. **Fl:** July. **I:** Hrútaber. (Rose family).

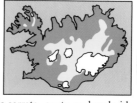

Compound leaf
(r. 0.4)

117 Meadowsweet
Filipendula ulmaria

Rather tall herb. Flowers crowded in corymb-like clusters, 5-parted, 6-8 mm wide, creamy to yellowish white. Petals with narrow claw and rounded ends, longer than the acute, hairy sepals. Stamens numerous. Several pistils in centre of flower, single-styled with thick stigma. Leaves odd-pinnate, with minute lobes between leaflets, stalked, with stipules at the base. Leaflets serrate, dark green and shiny on top, light green and tomentose underneath, the terminal leaflet three-lobed. **H:** 30-70 cm. **Hab:** Grassy, moderately moist heathland, meadows, hollows and woodland. Common in some districts. **Sim:** None. **Fl:** July. **I:** Mjaðjurt. (Rose family). — The Meadowsweet prefers sheltered locations, and is found wild only in the warmer districts of the country. It is also cultivated in gardens. The Meadowsweet is a rather large and strong plant, and flowers richly where grazing is not too heavy, but is only found as small leaves in the sward without flowering, where grazing is continuous.

Compound leaf (r. 0.3)

118 Rowan
Sorbus aucuparia

Flowers many in dense, corymb-like clusters, epigynous, 10-15 mm wide. Petals white, obtuse, with narrow claw. Sepals consist of very short, triangular lobes. Stamens numerous. One, usually three-styled pistil. Pedicels and calyx pubescent. Fruit resembles red berry. Leaves are odd-pinnate; leaflets dentate, usually lanceolate or oblong-ovate, 2.5-6 cm long, thin-haired. **H:** 2-12 m. **Hab:** Birch woodland or gorges; also cultivated in gardens. **Sim:** None. **Fl:** June. **I:** Reyniviður. (Rose family) — Wild Rowan does not form woods in Iceland by itself, but occurs singly among birches. They are usually taller, extending through the roof of the birchwood with richly flowering branches.

Compound leaf (r. 0.3)

119 Garden Angelica
Angelica archangelica

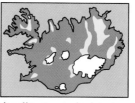

Many small flowers in 10-20 cm wide compound umbels, the partial umbels about 1.5-2.5 cm wide. Flowers 5-6 mm, whitish. Petals greenish white, ligulate or elliptic. Stamens five in each flower. One two-styled pistil; the fruit splits at maturity into two merocarps, each with four (five) ribs on one side. Leaves compound, bi- or three-pinnate. Leaflets coarsely dentate, glabrous. The sheaths very broad and inflated, enclosing the whole umbel before ripening. Stem very sturdy, furrowed, with large central cavity. Bracteoles linear, but bracts subtending compound umbel usually lacking. **H:** 50-180 cm. **Hab:** Fertile gorge slopes, depressions, banks of springs and rivers, lake banks and islands, bird-manured cliffs. Rather common. **Sim:** Wild Angelica (120). The Garden Angelica differs through spherical compound umbels, and larger, more coarsely toothed leaves. **Fl:** July-August. **I:** Ætihvönn. (Parsley family).

Fruit (m. 4.5)

120 Wild Angelica
Angelica sylvestris

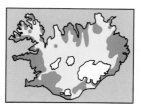

Flowers 3-5 mm wide, crowded in numerous umbels, which themselves are again arranged in 10-15 cm wide compound umbels. Corolla 5-parted; petals elliptic or lanceolate, white or slightly pinkish. Stamens five. Pistil two-styled, divided into two merocarps. Bracteoles linear. Umbel branches furrowed, short-pubescent. Leaves bi- or three-pinnate, the petiole deeply grooved along the upper side, leaflets dentate, sheaths dark purplish red. **H:** 50-130 cm. **Hab:** Banks and meadows along rivers, woodland, fertile, not too dry slopes. Widespread in lowland. **Sim:** Garden Angelica (119). The Wild Angelica differs in the umbel which is more flat, petioles with sharper grooves, the leaves with bluish bloom and more finely dentate than on Garden Angelica. **Fl:** July. **I:** Geithvönn. (Parsley family).

Fruit (m. 4)

121 Scots Lovage
Ligusticum scoticum

Flowers 3-4 mm wide. Petals obovate or ligulate, with terminal notch, white or slightly pinkish. Stamens five, pistil two-styled. Fruit splits into two merocarps, 6-8 mm long, with five longitudinal ribs. Bracts of compound umbel linear to ensiform, flat, 1-1.5 cm long. Leaves stalked, trifoliolate, sheath margin red; the leaflets petioled and again trifoliolate. Secondary leaflets dissected or lobed, the segments dentate. **H:** 30-60 cm. **Hab:** Seashore cliffs, grassy and rocky shore banks. Rather rare. **Sim:** Easily distinguished from other umbellate plants by the double trifoliolate leaves. **Fl:** June-July. **I:** Sæhvönn. (Parsley family).

Fruit (m. 4)

122 Caraway
Carum carvi

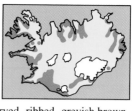

Flowers 2-3 mm wide, 5-parted, in 3-5 cm wide compound umbels. Petals white or faintly pinkish, of equal size, single-ribbed on upper side with involute terminal point. Stamens five, pistil two-styled, divided. Fruit splits into two, curved, ribbed, greyish brown, 3-4 mm long merocarps. Leaves bi- or three-pinnate; leaflets linear or narrowly lanceolate, pointed. **H:** 20-50 cm. **Hab:** Grassland, pastures and homefields. Naturalized in S Iceland, elsewhere usually restricted to cultivated land and farms. **Sim:** Easily recognized in flower; the leaves resemble Sea Mayweed (74); Caraway has slightly flattened rather than filiform lobes. **Fl:** May-June. **I:** Kúmen. (Parsley family). — The Caraway merocarps have a strong taste, and are used as a condiment in bread and cheese.

Fruit (m. 6)

123 Sweet Cicely
Myrrhis odorata

Flowers 2-4 mm wide in rather large (5-10 cm) compound umbels. Petals five, greenish white, 2 mm long, with terminal notch. Stamens five. Pistil two-styled, maturing into dark brown, shiny and sharply ribbed, 20-25 mm long merocarps. Bracteoles ciliate, bracts of compound umbel absent. Stems and petioles hairy, the leaves light green, three-pinnate, pubescent. The petioles have a strong taste of anise. **H:** 50-120 cm. **Hab:** Alien around farms and gardens, or in villages. Difficult weed in gardens once established. **Sim:** Cow Parsley (124). The Sweet Cicely differs in the pubescence and light green colour of leaves, the taste of the petioles, and much larger, almost winged fruits. **Fl:** June. **I:** Spánarkerfill. (Parsley family).

Fruit (m. 1.5)

124 Cow Parsley
Anthriscus sylvestris

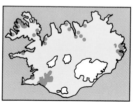

Large compound umbels consisting of several partial umbels, each with 8-16 flowers. Corolla white with yellowish green tint, 2-7 mm wide. Petals obcordate or obovate, of distinctly unequal size. Sepals absent. Stamens usually five, sometimes partially or totally absent. One bifid pistil with short styles. Fruit brown, shiny, 5-8 mm long, nearly rotund or softly angular, not ribbed. Bracteoles greenish or tinged with violet, ciliate; bracts absent. Leaves bi- or partly three-pinnate, long-petioled, nearly glabrous except towards margin and on lower side. Petioles and stems grooved, sparsely haired or glabrous. **H:** 30-120 cm. **Hab:** Alien in gardens, near houses and farms or in waste places. Widespread. **Sim:** Sweet Cicely (123). Cow Parsley differs through nearly glabrous leaves, and relatively small, smooth fruits. **Fl:** June. **I:** Skógarkerfill. (Parsley family).

Fruit (m. 5)

125 Yarrow
Achillea millefolium

Several flowers in small (4-5 mm) heads that superficially resemble simple flowers. Numerous heads on every plant, arranged in corymbs. Petals of rayflorets white or pink, rarely bright red, cordate. Discflorets tubular, whitish or yellowish grey. Bracts green, with dark membranous margin, long-haired. Stem tomentose, with alternate, 7-15 mm broad and 3-8 cm long, bi-pinnate tomentose leaves. Leaflets deeply dissected, with nearly linear, pointed lobules. **H:** 10-30 cm. **Hab:** Dry slopes and flats, often in sandy soil. Common throughout most of the country, not common in the South outside populated districts. **Sim:** Sneezewort (see 126). **Fl:** June. **I:** Vallhumall. (Daisy family).

Leaf (r. 0.6)

126 Sneezewort
Achillea ptarmica

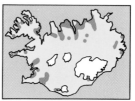

Many flowers arranged in rather small (1-1.5 cm) heads. The rayflorets ligulate; the corolla white, 4-5 mm long and 3-4 mm broad. Discflorets tubular, greenish white, 4 mm long, the corolla tube 5-lobed with triangular lobes. Bracts ligulate, green with black border, densely grey-pubescent. Leaves shaped like swords, tapering to a point, dentate, sessile or even clasping, with coarse teeth at the base, 2-5 cm long. **H:** 20-40 cm. **Hab:** Damp grassland, streamsides, or around farms and gardens. Rather rare but locally naturalized alien, sometimes spreading along creeks and rivers. **Sim:** None. The flower heads resemble Yarrow, but the two species are easily distinguished by the leaves. **I:** Silfurhnappur. (Daisy family).

Leaf (1:1)

127 Alpine Rock-cress
Arabis alpina

Flowers in short raceme, 4-parted, white. Petals 7-10 mm long, obtuse. Sepals yellowish, 3 mm long, hairy in upper part. Stamens six, one elongate pistil. Mature fruits 2-4 cm long, but less than 2 mm broad. Leaves hairy, coarsely dentate, elliptic or oblanceolate, 1.5-5 cm long, 5-15 mm broad. **H:** 8-30 cm. **Hab:** Ravines, cliffs and gorges, preferring shade and damp. Widespread. **Sim:** Northern Rock-cress (129). The Alpine Rock-cress differs in its larger flowers, much larger and more coarsely haired leaves. Sea Rocket (128). The Alpine Rock-cress differs in its hairy leaves and straight, slender siliques without constriction. **Fl:** May-June. **I:** Skriðnablóm. (Mustard family).

Leaf (m. 1.5)

120

128 Sea Rocket
Cakile arctica

Flowers in terminal racemes, 1.2-1.7 mm wide, 4-parted. Petals white to pale pinkish violet, 7-10 mm long, obtuse or emarginate at the front, with narrow claw. Sepals ovate-elliptic, yellowish with membranous margin, 3 mm long. Stamens six, one oblong pistil. Mature fruits 1.5-2 cm long and 4-5 mm broad, stalked, constricted below centre. Leaves glabrous, petioled, laterally incised or lobed, lanceolate to ovate, often 3-8 cm long. **H:** 10-40 cm. **Hab:** Sandy beaches; restricted to the seashore. Widespread along the south and west coast. **Sim:** Alpine Rock-cress (127). The Sea Rocket differs through its glabrous leaves and its habitat. **Fl:** June-July. **I:** Fjörukál. (Mustard family). — The Sea Rocket is an annual plant that reproduces by seeds every year. Consequently it may move along the coast and appear in different places from one year to the next. It sometimes covers wide stretches in the South and West, but is rarer along the northern coast. It is edible and tastes rather like cabbage.

Leaves (r. 0.5)

129 Northern Rock-cress
Cardaminopsis petraea

Several 4-parted flowers in short terminal raceme. Petals white, rarely with faint pinkish tint, 5-8 mm long, obtuse to emarginate. Sepals elliptic, 3 mm, green or pinkish with membranous margin. Stamens six, one pistil. Fruits 1.5-2 cm long, and 1-2 mm broad. Stem with few, lanceolate to elliptic, entire leaves. Basal leaves in rosette, oblanceolate, spatulate or obovate, usually coarsely dentate or lobed at the margin, sometimes entire; the blade usually 0.5-1 cm long, often slightly hairy like petiole. **H:** 5-12 cm. **Hab:** Gravel hills, screes, sand and lava fields. Very common. **Sim:** Whitlowgrass (130-131). The Northern Rock-cress has a little larger flowers, longer and more slender fruit, and a less compact basal rosette of leaves. See also Alpine Bitter-cress (135). **Fl:** May. **I:** Melablóm. (Mustard family). — The Northern Rock-cress is one of the most common wild flowers in Iceland, no less common in the highland deserts than in the lowland.

Fruit (m. 2.2)

130 Hoary Whitlowgrass
Draba incana

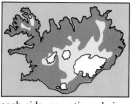

Flowers in short, terminal raceme, 4-parted. Petals white, 3-4 mm long. Sepals elliptic, with membranous margin, green or violet-tinted. Stamens six, one pistil. Fruits elliptic, 6-9 mm long and 2-3 mm broad, with distinct nerve on each side, sometimes hairy. The stem tomentose, usually dense-leaved. Stem leaves hairy, elliptic to lanceolate, coarsely dentate, 8-20 mm long; basal leaves narrower, forming compact and regular rosette around base of stem. Numerous, flowering lateral branches are often seen growing out from the basal part, after the main stem has been decapitated by grazing animals. **H:** 8-20 cm. **Hab:** Dry grassland, hillsides and gravelly soil. Common. **Sim:** Rock Whitlowgrass (131). The Hoary Whitlowgrass differs by the dense-leaved stem, and more compact rosettes of basal leaves. **Fl:** May-June. **I:** Grávorblóm. (Mustard family).

Open fruit (m. 3.5)

131 Rock Whitlowgrass
Draba norvegica

Flowers 4-parted, in short, terminal raceme. Petals white, 3-4 mm long. Sepals elliptic to ovate, green or violet-tinted, with narrow membranous margin. Stamens six, one oblong pistil. Fruits elliptic in outline, usually hairy, 5-8 mm long. Stem with forked hairs, rarely almost glabrous. One or two stem leaves, sometimes none; the leaves mainly in basal rosette, lanceolate, usually with forked and stellate hairs. **H:** Varies from 2-3 cm in the mountains, to as much as 12-20 cm beneath shrubs in the lowland. **Hab:** Grassy depressions, slopes, dwarf-shrub heath, rock outcrops or gravelly soil, reaching high altitudes. Common. **Sim:** Hoary Whitlowgrass (see 130). **Fl:** May-June. **I:** Hagavorblóm. (Mustard family). — The Rock Whitlowgrass varies greatly in Iceland. As delimited here, it might well consist of more than one species, but answers to that question will require further investigation.

Open fruit (m. 4)

132 Snow Whitlowgrass
Draba nivalis

Flowers 4-parted, several in short terminal raceme. Petals white, 2-3 mm long. Sepals less than 2 mm, elliptic, with membranous margin, green or violet-tinged. Stamens six, one pistil. Fruit elliptical in shape, 4-5 mm long and 1-1.5 mm broad. Leaves in basal rosette, usually nearly entire, 3-4 mm long and 2-2.5 mm broad; stem-leaves absent. Stem and leaves covered with dense, grey coat of very short, forked and stellate hairs. **H:** 2-5 cm. **Hab:** Hilltops, rock outcrops and cairns. Rather rare. **Sim:** Rock Whitlowgrass (131). The Snow Whitlowgrass is much more rare, and differs through the rime-grey leaf rosette, and shorter and broader leaves. **Fl:** June-July. **I:** Héluvorblóm. (Mustard family)

Closed and open fruit (m. 5)

133 Shepherd's Purse
■☐
Capsella bursa-pastoris
☐

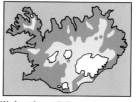

Small flowers, 2-3 mm wide, in long terminal racemes; the petals white, obovate, with narrow claw. Sepals ligulate, light tawny, with membranous margin. Stamens six, one short-styled pistil. Fruit is an obcordate or triangular silicle, about 5-7 mm in length and breadth, the pedicel two or three-times the fruit length. Leaves very variable in size and shape; those in basal rosette either pinnatifid or more or less entire; the stem leaves alternate, pinnately lobed, dentate or nearly entire, either tapering towards the base or sessile with auricles. **H:** 15-40 cm. **Hab:** Vegetable gardens, waste places with fertile soil, manured areas. Common. **Sim:** None. Easily recognized by heart-shaped silicles. **Fl:** May-Sept. **I:** Hjartarfi. (Mustard family). — **Field Penny-cress** *Thlaspi arvense* is a rare alien, related to the Shepherd's Purse, but the fruits are much larger (1-1.5 cm), round, broad-winged and with terminal incision.

Fruit (m. 3)

134 Hairy Bitter-cress
☐■
Cardamine hirsuta
☐

Annual plant with 4-parted flowers in terminal raceme. Petals white, 2-3 mm long, spatulate. Sepals 1-1.5 mm, pinkish. Stamens six. Single pistil, maturing into 2 cm long and 1 mm broad silique. Leaves pinnate, the terminal leaflet of the basal leaves largest, round to reniform, 5-8 mm wide; the lateral leaflets smaller, rhomboid to round. **H:** 5-20 cm. **Hab:** Open soil, waste places, flower beds and potato fields. Widespread in S and SW Iceland. **Sim:** Lady Smock (62). Only the leaf-rosettes are similar, the flowers quite different. **I:** Lambaklukka. (Mustard family).

Fruit (m. 2.3)

135 Alpine Bitter-cress
☐☐
Cardamine bellidifolia
■

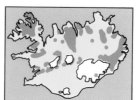

Flowers 4-5 mm wide, 4-parted. Petals white. Sepals dark, blunt, 2 mm long. Stamens six. One pistil maturing into 1-2 cm long and only 1 mm broad silique. Leaves mainly basal, entire, on 1-2 cm long petiole; the blade ovate to roundish, 3-7 mm long and 2-5 mm broad, glabrous, usually tipped with short, glandular point. **H:** 1-6 cm. **Hab:** Gravelly and rocky ground, or mossy heaths at high altitudes. Widespread. **Sim:** Dwarfish high-mountain variety of Scurvy Grass (136). Small mountain-plants of Northern Rock-cress (129). The Alpine Bitter-cress differs in shape of leaves, and in petiole always being longer than the blade; the long, slender fruits are ripe high in the mountains long before those of the Northern Rock-cress. **I:** Jöklaklukka. (Mustard family).

Fruit (m. 3)

136 Common Scurvygrass
Cochlearia officinalis

Flowers in short racemes, yellowish white or pure white, 4-parted. Petals spatulate, 4 mm long. Sepals greenish or tinged with reddish violet, elliptic or obovate, 2 mm long. Stamens six, one spherical pistil. Mature fruits are 5-7 mm long and 4-5 mm broad, lemon-shaped or nearly spherical. Stem-leaves few, rhomboid to lanceolate, with a few teeth or angles, sessile or short-stalked. Basal leaves in rosette, long-petioled; the peticle two or three times the leaf size; the blade reniform, cordate or round, nearly entire, usually 2-4 cm wide, but can be as small as 2 mm on dwarfish plants. Entire plant glabrous. **H:** 10-30 cm. **Hab:** Bird-cliffs, rocky shores. Widespread around the country. Occasionally found in the mountains of the Central Highlands, or along periodically dry river beds. In these habitats the Scurvygrass may be quite dwarfish, the blade only 2-3 mm wide and the whole plant decumbent, only 2-3 cm in diameter. The origin of these small mountain plants is not clear. They might belong to a species distinct from the seashore plants. **Sim:** None; the tiny mountain variety can be mistaken for Alpine Bitter-cress (135). The Scurvygrass differs in round leaves and globose fruits. **Fl:** May-June. **I:** Skarfakál. (Mustard family).

Closed and open fruit (m. 3.6)

137 Awlwort
Subularia aquatica

Very small, annual, aquatic plant. Flowers few, 4-parted. Petals white, 1-2 mm long and less than 0.5 mm broad. Sepals green, often dark or violet-tinted towards tip. Stamens six. Single pistil, maturing into obovate to elliptic fruit, 2-3 mm long and 1.5-2 mm broad. Fruit-stalk slightly longer than fruit itself. Leaves filiform, in basal tuft, 0.5-4 cm long, 1 mm broad below, tapering to an acute point. **H:** 2-5 cm. **Hab:** Mud along lake-sides, bottom of shallow lakes and pools. Widespread. Can bloom and bear fruits to maturity while submerged in water. **Sim:** When not in flower the Awlwort resembles many of the species with small tufts of grass-like leaves (Creeping Spearwort (167), Needle Spikerush (313), Spring Quillwort (209), Shoreweed (210)), but can be easily recognized in bloom or fruit by the characteristics of the Mustard family: 4-parted flowers, six stamens and silicle as fruit. The Awlwort never forms runners, as some of the other species do. **Fl:** July. **I:** Alurt. (Mustard family). — **Pigmyweed** *Crassula aquatica* is a very small, and very rare aquatic plant with 4-parted flowers, opposite, subulate leaves and four pistils. Restricted to thermal soil. (Stonecrop family).

Fruit (m. 6)

138 Common Whitlowgrass
■□
□
Erophila verna

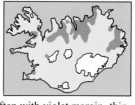

Annual, delicate plant, sometimes quite small
with few branches, sometimes larger and richly
branched. Flowers in racemes, 4-parted. Petals
white, 2-4 mm long, bifid almost half way
down. Sepals 1.5-2 mm long, elliptic, green, often with violet margin, thin-haired. Stamens six. One pistil maturing to elliptic, 4-6 mm long and 2-2.5 mm broad, silique. Stems glabrous, leafless. All the leaves in basal rosette, 5-12 mm long and 2-4 mm broad, almost entire, lanceolate or elliptic, with forked hairs. **H:** 3-15 cm. **Hab:** Gravel flats, dry hillsides or sandy gardens. Widespread throughout N and NE Iceland. **Sim:** Other Whitlowgrasses (130, 131). The Common Whitlowgrass differs in the bilobed petals and repeatedly branched stems. **Fl:** April-May. **I:** Vorperla. (Mustard family).

Closed and open fruit (m. 2.5)

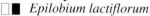

139 Milky Willowherb
□■
□
Epilobium lactiflorum

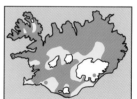

Flowers small, 4-parted, epigynous. Corolla
white to faint pinkish, 3-5 mm long. Calyx
slightly shorter. Stamens eight. One pistil of
four carpels, 3-5 cm long. Stigma club-shaped,
undivided. Fruit splits into four sections when ripe. Seeds with white tuft of hairs. Stem angular, usually with narrow stripes of hair. Leaves opposite, glabrous, ovate or elliptic, usually obtuse, 1.5-3 cm long, 6-12 mm broad, usually indistinctly dentate to entire. **H:** 8-15 cm. **Hab:** Shady cliffs, gorges and dells in steep slopes. Widespread. **Sim:** Easily distinguished from other willowherbs by the white flowers. Difficult to distinguish from Hornemann's Willowherb (46) and Chickweed Willowherb (45) when not in flower. The stem and leaves of the Milky Willowherb are lighter green and less red-tinted. **Fl:** June-July. **I:** Ljósadúnurt. (Willowherb family).

Open fruit (1:1)

140 Snow Pearlwort
□□
■
Sagina nivalis

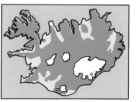

Flowers 4-parted. Petals white or transparent,
shorter or of same length as the sepals, which
are broad-elliptic, 2 mm long, green, with
dark-violet membranous margin. Stamens
eight. One pistil maturing into capsule which opens into 4-5 teeth. Leaves opposite, lanceolate or linear, sharp-pointed. Basal leaves 5-12 mm long. **H:** 2-3 cm. **Hab:** Open, damp soil in mountains, open roadsides or moist, gravelly riversides. Rather common at higher altitudes. **Sim:** Alpine Pearlwort (105) and Procumbent Pearlwort (193). The Snow Pearlwort differs from both through darker green colour, and dark-brown to violet-bordered sepals. It is further distinguished through its four-parted flowers from Alpine Pearlwort and Tufted Pearlwort (106A), which both have 5-parted flowers. **Fl:** June-July. **I:** Snækrækill. (Pink family).

Fruit in calyx (m. 6)

141 Blinks
Montia fontana

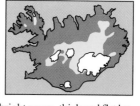

Very small flowers. Petals white, three to five, 1-2 mm long. Sepals two, green, 1-1.5 mm wide, round. Stamens three, single pistil. Fruit splits into three sections when mature, enclos-ing three, shiny, black seeds. Leaves opposite, bright green, thick and fleshy, lanceolate to elliptic, entire, 4-8 mm long. **H:** Frequently 2-10 cm, sometimes longer and then usually lying flat. **Hab:** Cold, mossy springs, small creeks. Common. **Sim:** Easily recognized by the small, three-parted flowers. **Fl:** June. **I:** Lækjagrýta. (Purslane family).

Fruit in calyx (m. 6)

142 Scottish Asphodel
Tofieldia pusilla

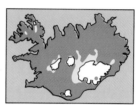

Many yellow-white flowers, close together in short, nearly globose (5-7 mm) spike on top of leafless stem. Perianth leaves six, elliptic to lanceolate, 2-3 mm long. Stamens six. Single pistil of three carpels with three stigmas; the fruit 3 mm long, splitting into three, curved, short-beaked sections when mature. All the leaves at the base, 2-3 cm long and 2 mm broad, sword-shaped, upright, entire, arranged in a fan-shaped whorl. **H:** 8-18 cm. **Hab:** Heathland meadows and pastures. **Sim:** Easily recognized by the arrangement of leaves in one plane, which is unique among native Icelandic plants. **Fl:** June. **I:** Sýkigras. (Bunchflower family).

Fruit in calyx (m. 5)

143 Northern Bedstraw
Galium boreale

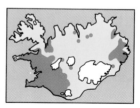

Many small, 4-parted, white flowers in branched inflorescences in upper leaf axils. Corolla gamopetalous, 2.5-3.5 mm wide, split almost to the base into four, spreading lobes. Sepals, reduced to a narrow rim at base of petals, have hooked hairs. Stamens four, one two-styled pistil. Stems four-sided with raised angles. Four differ-ent-sized leaves in whorls on the stem, two opposite leaves longer than the others, lanceolate, broader towards the base, blunt-tipped, 8-18 cm long, three-veined, the central vein more prominent than the others. **H:** 8-25 cm. **Hab:** Grassy heaths and slopes. Common in the South and West, rare else-where. **Sim:** Slender Bedstraw (144) and Fen Bedstraw (145). The Northern Bedstraw is easily identified by four blunt-tipped leaves in the whorls. Small Bedstraw (146) and Marsh Bedstraw (146A). The Northern Bedstraw differs in three-nerved leaves. **Fl:** July. **I:** Krossmaðra. (Madder family).

Whorl of leaves (m. 1.2)

144 Slender Bedstraw
Galium normanii

Many small flowers in branched inflorescences in upper leaf axils. Flowers white or yellowish-white. Corolla gamopetalous, 3-4 mm wide, deeply divided into four, spreading lobes.

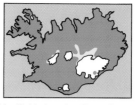

Calyx glabrous. Stamens four, single pistil with divided style. Stem four-sided with raised angles. Leaves 6-8 in whorls on stem, 5-10 mm long, rough-edged, oblanceolate, the broadest part near the sharp-pointed tip. **H:** 5-12 cm, rarely more. **Hab:** Dry hillsides and heathland, also in gravelly soil and cliffs. Common. **Sim:** Northern Bedstraw (143). The Slender Bedstraw differs in having at least six pointed leaves in a whorl. See also Fen Bedstraw (145). **Fl:** June. **I:** Hvítmaðra. (Madder family).

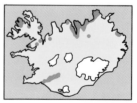

Whorl of leaves (m. 1.6)

145 Fen Bedstraw
Galium uliginosum

Several flowers in branched inflorescences in axils of upper leaves. Corolla gamopetalous, 3-4 mm wide, deeply divided into four, spreading lobes. Calyx glabrous. Four stamens, one pistil

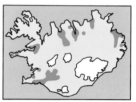

with divided style. Leaves usually four to six in each whorl, oblanceolate, rough-edged, 6-14 mm long, the broadest part near the sharp-pointed tip. Stem sharply angular and quite rough due to sharp, downwards directed hooks. **H:** 12-30 cm. **Hab:** Grassy riverbanks, grassy, damp heathland and slopes. Rather rare. **Sim:** Slender Bedstraw (144). The Fen Bedstraw differs mainly through the extremely rough stem, and it rarely has more than six leaves in a whorl (often 7-8 on Slender Bedstraw); it is also larger and more fragile, usually receiving support from tall grass. **Fl:** July. **I:** Laugamaðra. (Madder family).

Whorl of leaves (m. 1.2)

146 Small Bedstraw
Galium trifidum

Very small plant. Few flowers, 1.5-2 mm wide. Corolla gamopetalous, three-lobed. Calyx glabrous. Stamens three, one pistil with divided style. Leaves four in a whorl, lanceo-

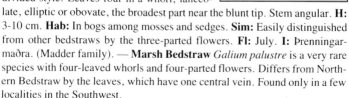

late, elliptic or obovate, the broadest part near the blunt tip. Stem angular. **H:** 3-10 cm. **Hab:** In bogs among mosses and sedges. **Sim:** Easily distinguished from other bedstraws by the three-parted flowers. **Fl:** July. **I:** Þrenningar-maðra. (Madder family). — **Marsh Bedstraw** *Galium palustre* is a very rare species with four-leaved whorls and four-parted flowers. Differs from Northern Bedstraw by the leaves, which have one central vein. Found only in a few localities in the Southwest.

Whorl of leaves (m. 1.5)

147 Cassiope
Cassiope hypnoides

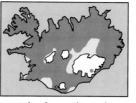

Flowers 5-7 mm wide. Corolla white or yellowish white, gamopetalous, deeply divided into blunt lobes. Sepals less than half the length of petals, dark red, acute. Pedicels 6-12 mm long, dark. Stamens ten with two, long, filamentous hooks on the anthers. Single pistil made up of five carpels, maturing to a capsule which opens into five longitudinal fissures. Shoots dense-leaved. Leaves 2-3 mm long, needle-shaped, entire, pointed. **H:** Ascending shoots about 2-4 cm. **Hab:** Snowbeds, short-grown hollows and moist slopes in mountains; often in dense crowds. Rather rare in the lowland, otherwise common. **Sim:** None. Easily recognized by the small, drooping, white bells with red sepals. **Fl:** May-June. **I:** Mosalyng. (Heath family).

Fruit in calyx (m. 5)

148 Bearberry
Arctostaphylos uva-ursi

Several flowers in dense, short, nodding cluster. Corolla gamopetalous, bell-shaped or barrel-shaped with narrow opening, 4-5 mm wide, white to pink, usually with pink, short-lobed collar. Sepals very short, pink, membranous. Stamens ten with dark anthers provided with two slender hooks. One pistil, maturing into a red fruit resembling a berry, but it is dry and mealy inside. Leaves thick, shiny, entire, usually obovate or elliptic, short-stalked; the blade 12-18 mm long and 6-8 mm broad. Stem woody. **H:** Upright shoots usually 5-15 cm long. **Hab:** Dwarf-shrub heaths and woodland. Common. **Sim:** Cowberry, see 148A. **Fl:** May-June. **I:** Sortulyng. (Heath family). — **Cowberry** *Vaccinium vitis-idaea* is a very rare species in Iceland, with evergreen leaves, superficially resembling Bearberry. Differs through slightly dentate and revolute leaf margin. It has red berries, juicy and edible. Found only in a few localities in E and NE Iceland. — **Bog Rosemary** *Andromeda polifolia* is a very rare species recently discovered in the northern part of the eastern fjords. Many flowers are clustered on the stem apex, bell-shaped to globose on long pedicels, white or pink. The leaves are evergreen, thick, cartilaginous, narrow, lanceolate, light grey underneath.

Inflorescence (m. 2)

149 Common Wintergreen
Pyrola minor

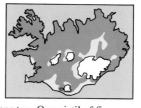

Flowers form short (1.5-3 cm) raceme. Corolla bell-shaped, split almost to the base, 5-parted. Petals broad-elliptic or nearly round, white, sometimes pinkish towards the tip, 4-5 mm long. Sepals dark red, 2 mm long, acute. Stamens ten. One pistil of five carpels, maturing to capsule. Leaves broad-elliptic or nearly round, indistinctly denticulate, stalked. Small scale-like leaves between the basal foliage leaves, single leaf higher up the stem. **H:** 8-15 cm. **Hab:** Woodland, hollows in slopes and hillsides, frequently in snowbeds in the mountains. Common. **Sim:** Arctic Wintergreen (see 150). Serrated Wintergreen (see 151). **Fl:** July. **I:** Klukkublóm. (Wintergreen family).

Fruit (m. 4)

150 Arctic Wintergreen
Pyrola grandiflora

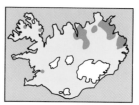

Flowers form few-flowered terminal raceme. Corolla split almost to the base, 14-18 mm wide. Petal lobes obovate, white or pink-veined. Stamens ten with bright yellow anthers. Single, purple pistil with long (7 mm) curved style. Sepals 3 mm long, pinkish or tawny. Foliage leaves basal, almost round to broad-elliptic, 2-3.5 cm across, rather thick, leathery, stalked; the stem with only a few oblong, 7-10 mm long tawny or pink scale leaves. **H:** 10-20 cm. **Hab:** Dwarf-shrub heath or woodland with moist soil. Rather rare. **Sim:** Common Wintergreen (149). The Arctic Wintergreen differs through the long, curved style, and larger more open flowers. If not in flower these species are hard to distinguish; the Arctic Wintergreen has slightly thicker, darker, evergreen leaves. **Fl:** July-August. **I:** Björlulilja. (Wintergreen family).

Fruit (m. 3)

151 Serrated Wintergreen
Orthilia secunda

Flowers on short pedicels in one-sided, 2-3 cm long terminal raceme. Corolla bell-shaped, split almost to the base. Petals yellowish green or whitish, 5 mm long with membranous margin. Sepals very short (1-1.5 mm), obtuse, denticulate. Stamens ten. One pistil with rather thick, long, dark style. Basal leaves ovate or elliptic, denticulate, 1.2-3 cm long and 1-2 cm broad. Small (3-5 mm), pointed, greenish scale leaves on stem and between basal leaves. **H:** 8-15 cm. **Hab:** Woodland and dwarf-shrub heath. Widespread throughout country, more common in N and NW Iceland than elsewhere. **Sim:** Common Wintergreen (149). The Serrated Wintergreen differs in the one-sided inflorescence, greenish corolla, longer style, more pointed and distinctly dentate leaves. **Fl:** July-August. **I:** Grænlilja. (Wintergreen family).

Fruit (m. 5)

152 Autumn Gentian
Gentianella amarella

Annual plant with flowers in leaf axils. Corolla tubular, 1.5-2 cm long and 4-5 mm broad, split 1/4 down into five lobes. Petal lobes yellowish green or greenish white, with filiform appendages in throat of tube. Calyx usually half the length of the corolla, split more than half way down into narrow, pointed, green lobes of unequal length. Leaves opposite, lanceolate to ovate-lanceolate, 1.5-2 cm long. Stem usually tinged with reddish violet, angular. Entire plant glabrous. **H:** 8-25 cm. **Hab:** Dry grassland, grassy hillsides and heathland. Rather common. **Sim:** Field Gentian (32). The Autumn Gentian differs distinctly in the calyx, which consists of five narrow segments, and in colour of flowers, although Field Gentian may occasionally have light or white flowers. **Fl:** August. **I:** Grænvöndur. (Gentian family).

Calyx (m. 3)

153 Cold Eyebright
Euphrasia frigida

Annual plant, repeatedly branched or unbranched; the inflorescence densely leaved. Corolla zygomorphic, tubular below, bilabiate above, 4-7 mm long, whitish with violet veins, esp. upper lip, the lower lip with yellow spot in throat. Calyx with v-shaped, sharp-pointed lobes, greenish with dark edges and veins, hairy. Four stamens with purple-black anthers. Single pistil of two carpels, maturing into oblong capsule. Leaves generally opposite, or some alternate; lanceolate, obovate or ovate, with coarse teeth, hairy, usually tinged with blue. **H:** 3-15 cm. **Hab:** Unfertile grass flats, stream banks, open soil. Common. **Sim:** Arctic Eyebright (see 153A). **Fl:** July-August. **I:** Augnfró. (Figwort family). — **Arctic Eyebright** *Euphrasia arctica* is very rare, resembling Cold Eyebright. Flowers are a deeper violet and larger, about 8-9 mm long; calyx as well as uppermost leaves have glandular hairs only.

Fruit in calyx (m. 5)

154 White Dead-nettle
Lamium album

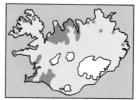

Flowers sessile, densely clustered in leaf axils. Corolla zygomorphic, bilabiate with wide open lips, white, 1.5-2 cm long. Calyx 5-lobed, 7-10 mm long, green with dark-spotted bottom; calyx lobes sharp-pointed, revolute, spreading. Stamens four, beneath helmet of upper lip; anthers dark. Pistil splits into four merocarps at maturity. Stem rather thick, quadrangular, hairy. Leaves opposite, cordate or ovate, acute and coarsely dentate, hairy, 4-8 cm long. **H:** 20-40 cm. **Hab:** Naturalized alien in homefields, gardens and waste places. Rather widespread. **Sim:** None. **Fl:** June. **I:** Ljósatvítönn. (Mint family).

Flower (m. 1.5)

155 White Clover
Trifolium repens

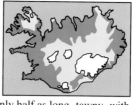

Stem prostrate. Inflorescence a compact, globular head (1.5-2.5 cm), terminal on erect side branches. Flowers gamopetalous, zygomorphic, on very short pedicels. Corolla whitish, 8-10 mm long, turning brown. Calyx only half as long, tawny, with dark green nerves, split less than half way down, sparsely haired or glabrous. Sepals with membranous margin between acute lobes. Stamens ten, hidden by corolla. One pistil. Leaves trifoliolate, long-petioled, rising from stolons. Leaflets obovate to obcordate, sessile, only terminal leaflet may be very short-petioled, usually with extremely fine, sharp teeth, which are extensions of the lateral nerves. **H:** Upright stems 10-15 cm, petioles 5-10 cm. **Hab:** Grass plains, slopes, hillsides and cultivated homefields. Common; native with wide distribution in the North, naturalized alien in some other regions. **Sim:** Alsike Clover (see 155A). **Fl:** June-July. **I:** Hvítsmári. (Pea family). — **Alsike Clover** *Trifolium hybridum* resembles White Clover, but is larger with ascending or upright stem. The leaflets ovate, obovate or elliptic, never obcordate; the flowers often slightly pinkish, the calyx almost glabrous. Alien around farms and in cultivated homefields.

Flower
(m. 4.5)

156 Marsh-marigold
Caltha palustris

Flowers large, 3-4 cm wide, bright yellow. Perianth simple, petals five. Numerous stamens with yellow anthers. Many pistils in centre of flowers. Fruits 7-8 mm long, short-beaked follicles, each with a few seeds. Stem leaves alternate, reniform, 3-8 cm wide, crenate, glabrous; basal leaves and lower stem leaves on long petioles. **H:** 15-30 cm. **Hab:** Road ditches, stream banks, dikes. Common in the lowland. **Sim:** Differs from other species of the buttercup family by the reniform leaves, simple perianth and several-seeded fruits. **Fl:** May-June. **I:** Hófsóley. (Buttercup family). — Marsh-marigold, also called "lækjasóley" (brook buttercup) in Icelandic, is one of the showiest flowers of the countryside. Its bright yellow colour in roadside ditches and dikes is a welcome sign of spring.

Leaf
(r. 0.4)

157 Alpine Cinquefoil
Potentilla crantzii

Flowers 5-parted, 1.5 cm wide. Petals yellow with orange spot at the base, obcordate with small terminal notch. Calyx double, five narrow epicalyx lobes alternating with the broader, pointed sepals. Stamens and pistils numerous. Leaves palmatifid with three or five coarsely dentate segments. **H:**15-25 cm. **Hab:** Dry grassland, heath and open screes or talus slopes. Common. **Sim:** Meadow Buttercup (159) and Creeping Buttercup (160). Leaves of the Alpine Cinquefoil are smaller and more hairy. Differs distinctly through epicalyx, and differently dissected leaves. **Fl:**May-June. **I:** Gullmura. (Rose family). — **Tormentil** *Potentilla erecta* is a very rare species; it has similar, 5-sected leaves, but differs in 4-parted, yellow flowers.

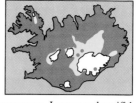

Leaf (1:1)

158 Silverweed
Potentilla anserina

Flowers 5-parted. Petals yellow, 2-2.5 cm wide. Calyx green, five narrow epicalyx lobes alternating with sepals, which are usually shorter and broader. Stamens and pistils numerous. Leaves odd-pinnate, with 5-12 pairs of leaflets, which are lanceolate to obovate, coarsely dentate, with a silvery coat of hair underneath or on both sides. **H:** Erect parts 5-15 cm; creeping runners much longer. **Hab:** Sandy soil, commonly close to the seashore or near rivers. Common, but rather rare in inland districts. **Sim:** None. **Fl:** June. **I:** Tágamura. (Rose family). — The Silverweed is divided into two subspecies, ssp. *anserina*, which corresponds to the description above, and ssp. *egedii* (**Sea-side Silverweed**), which is smaller, often with only 3-4 pairs of leaflets; the epicalyx lobes narrow, entire, shorter than the sepals. Restricted to salt marshes along the seashore.

Leaf (r. 0.5)

159 Meadow Buttercup
Ranunculus acris

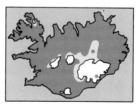

Flowers 5-parted, 2-2.5 cm wide. Petals shiny, usually obtuse. Calyx without epicalyx, sepals hairy with broad membranous margin. Stamens numerous. Many pistils maturing into small, one-seeded nutlets. Leaves alternate, petioled, hairy, deeply palmatifid in 3-5 sections, each of which is again dissected into three, coarsely dentate lobes. **H:** 15-40 cm. **Hab:** Cultivated homefields, pastures, grassy depressions and ravines, snowbeds in the mountains. Common. **Sim:** Creeping Buttercup (see 160). Goldilocks (see 160A) and Alpine Cinquefoil (see 157). **Fl:** May-June. **I:** Brennisóley. (Buttercup family).

Leaf (r. 0.4)

160 Creeping Buttercup
Ranunculus repens

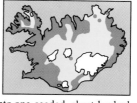

Stem creeping, with rooting runners and ascending branches. Flowers 1.5-2.5 cm wide. Petals bright yellow, sepals pinkish-tawny, 5-6 mm long. Many stamens with yellow anthers.

Pistils numerous in centre of flower, maturing into one-seeded, short-beaked nutlets. Stem hairy, with alternate leaves; basal leaves long-petioled. Petioles densely haired, the blade sparsely haired, divided into three leaflets, the terminal one stalked. Leaflets again deeply dissected into three, coarsely dentate lobes. **H:** 15-35 cm. **Hab:** Cultivated homefields, fertile pastures in villages, near houses and abandoned farms, gardens. Rather common, naturalized alien. **Sim:** Meadow Buttercup (159). The Creeping Buttercup differs by the trifoliolate blade, with stalked terminal leaflet. **Fl:** June. **I:** Skriðsóley. (Buttercup family). — **Goldilocks Buttercup** *Ranunculus auricomus* is a rare species resembling Meadow Buttercup, but differing in the diverse leaf shape. Basal leaves are reniform, coarsely dentate or deeply lobed; the uppermost leaves divided into several linear to Y-shaped segments.

Leaf
(r. 0.5)

161 Marsh Saxifrage
Saxifraga hirculus

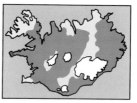

Flowers 5-parted, usually only one or two on each stem, 2-3 cm wide. Petals yellow with many red spots in lower half of inside, 5-7 mm broad. Sepals green, recurved, with longitudi

nal stripes, only half as long as the petals. Stamens ten, single pistil with divided apex. Stem brown-haired, leafy. Leaves entire, lanceolate; the blade 1-2 cm long and 2-4 mm broad; the basal leaves frequently stalked. **H:** 6-12 cm. **Hab:** Moist soil and bogs, moist river beds, damp open soil, or mossy cliffs with seepage water. Widespread, esp. in the highland. **Sim:** None. Has larger flowers than other yellow saxifrages; differs from buttercups and cinquefoil by the small, entire leaves. **Fl:** June-July. **I:** Gullbrá. (Saxifrage family). — Although the Marsh Saxifrage is found here and there in the lowland, esp. in the palagonite cliffs of the South, it is primarily a characteristic species of the Central Highlands, where it forms dense, yellow covers in localities with sufficient moisture.

Fruit in calyx
(m. 2.2)

162 Arctic Poppy
Papaver radicatum

Flowers 2.5-3 mm wide, yellow; a variety with white, and another with pink flowers occurs in the Northwest. Petals four. Two dark-haired sepals, falling off at flowering time. Stamens numerous. Single, large (8-12 mm) pistil without style, covered with stiff, black hairs and bearing four- to five-armed, star-shaped stigma on the flat top. Fruit is a capsule with a row of holes below upper margin; seeds very small, numerous. Flower scape leafless, brown-haired. Leaves in basal rosette, stalked, pinnatifid, with coarse hairs. **H:** 8-20 cm. **Hab:** Gravelly and sandy soil, cliffs, rock outcrops. Common in some districts, in others restricted to mountains. **Sim:** Iceland Poppy (see 163); easily distinguished from all other plants by the large, four-parted flowers. **Fl:** June. **I:** Melasól. (Poppy family).

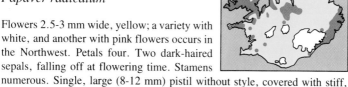

Leaf (m. 1.7)

163 Iceland Poppy
Papaver nudicaule

Flowers 4-6 cm large, white, yellow or orange. Petals four. Sepals two, black-haired, falling off at flowering time. Stamens numerous with yellow anthers. Single, large, black-haired pistil without style; star-shaped, six- to nine-armed stigma on the flat pistil top. Flower scapes without leaves, with tawny, appressed hairs. Basal leaves long-petioled, pinnatifid, glabrous. **H:** 25-40 cm. **Hab:** Alien in gardens, waste places and roadsides. Rare. **Sim:** Arctic Poppy (162). The Iceland Poppy differs in its glabrous leaves, more divided stigma, and larger flowers. **Fl:** June. **I:** Garðasól. (Poppy family).

Leaf (r. 0.4)

164 Yellow Saxifrage
Saxifraga aizoides

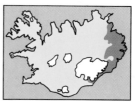

Flowers 5-parted, 10-15 cm wide. Petals rather narrow, yellow, red-spotted. Sepals broad-elliptic, erect, shorter than the petals. Stamens ten, upper part of pistil bifid. Stem ascending, with alternate, linear to lanceolate, 8-18 mm long and 1.5-3 mm broad, sharp-pointed, entire leaves with sparse, coarse marginal hairs. **H:** 5-15 cm. **Hab:** Cliffs, screes, gravelly soil and riverbeds. Widespread in the East. **Sim:** None. **Fl:** July. **I:** Gullsteinbrjótur. (Saxifrage family).

Leaf (m. 4)

148

165 Biting Stonecrop
Sedum acre

Flowers 1-1.5 cm wide, 5-parted. Petals pointed, lanceolate, yellow. Sepals short (3 mm), elliptic, blunt-tipped. Stamens ten; five single-styled pistils. Leaves short (3-4 mm) and thick, nearly rotund, fleshy, green, densely clustered at the apex of numerous, short shoots. **H:** Forms prostrate covers. **Hab:** Gravel hills, riverbeds, rock outcrops and cliffs, commonly on top of rocks manured by birds. Common. **Sim:** Annual Stonecrop (166). The Biting Stonecrop differs in the many flowerless leaf shoots; it has larger, bright yellow flowers with broader petals. **Fl:** July-August. **I:** Helluhnoðri. (Stonecrop family).

Leafy shoots (m. 1.5)

166 Annual Stonecrop
Sedum annuum

Annual plant. Flowers 5-9 mm wide, 5-parted. Petals yellowish, narrow, pointed. Sepals shorter, blunt. Stamens ten; five single-styled pistils. Leaves 3-5 mm long, thick, rotund, fleshy, yellowish green or tinged with red; Flowerless shoots very few or absent. **H:** 3-5 cm. **Hab:** Screes and rocky slopes, sunny locations. Widespread throughout S Iceland. **Sim:** Biting Stonecrop (165). The Annual Stonecrop differs in the smaller flowers, narrower petals, and erect stem, lacking the many dense-leaved shoots characteristic of the Biting Stonecrop. **Fl:** June. **I:** Skriðuhnoðri. (Stonecrop family). — The Annual Stonecrop is one of the more heat-loving plants in Iceland, as reflected through its distribution. It is most common in the warmer districts, usually in locations exposed to the South.

Fruit (m. 5)

167 Creeping Spearwort
Ranunculus reptans

Flowers 1 cm wide, 5-parted. Petals yellow, obovate, obtuse. Sepals shorter, yellowish green, soon falling off. Many stamens (15-20) and pistils. Stem prostrate, rooting at the nodes, with curved, elevated internodes. Leaves in rosettes at the nodes, entire, either linear, or with short, long-petioled, lanceolate blade, glabrous. **H:** Usually not rising more than 5 cm above ground, but runners may be quite long. **Hab:** Moist, open soil, mud in shallow lake bottoms, esp. those that dry up late in summer. Common. **Sim:** Mudwort (64) has leaves resembling Creeping Spearwort, but no runners and different flowers. Arctic Buttercup (175) differs in smaller, 3-parted flowers, and in the leaves. **Fl:** July. **I:** Flagasóley. (Buttercup family). — The long creeping runners with curved internodes are very characteristic for the Creeping Spearwort. Lake bottoms often appear embroidered for long distances by the stitches made by its jointed, rooting runners.

Leaf (m. 3)

168 Pigmy Buttercup
Ranunculus pygmaeus

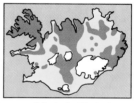

Flowers 0.5-1 cm wide, 5-parted. Petals yellow, slightly shorter than the sepals, which are greenish, slightly hairy with membranous margin. Stamens and pistils rather many, pistils small, sitting on an elevated receptacle. Leaves long-petioled, the blade three- to five-lobed, 1-1.5 cm broad, glabrous or with a few marginal hairs. **H:** 2-7 cm. **Hab:** Damp, vegetated slopes, dells and ravines, along creeks and springs. Rather widespread, but restricted to high mountains. **Sim:** Brook Saxifrage (96) resembles Pigmy Buttercup when not flowering: it has similar leaves, but differs in the white flowers. The Pigmy Buttercup differs in fruit by the many small nutlets, while the Saxifrages have single capsule with a divided top. **Fl:** July-August. **I:** Dvergsóley. (Buttercup family).

Leaf (m. 1.9)

152

169 Creeping Sibbaldia
Sibbaldia procumbens

Flowers 5-7 mm wide, 5-parted. Petals light yellow, narrow, ligulate, shorter than the sepals which are green, acute, alternating with narrow epicalyx lobes. Stamens five, pistils usually 8-20. Stems consist of procumbent, thick rhizomes. Leaves on long stalks, thinly haired, trifoliolate, each leaflet terminating in three, rarely four or five teeth. **H:** 5-10 cm. **Hab:** Snowbeds in the mountains. Common. **Sim:** None. Leaves recall Alpine Lady's-mantle (190) which always has more than three, and narrower, leaflets. **Fl:** June. **I:** Fjallasmári. (Rose family). — The Creeping Sibbaldia is, along with the Dwarf Cudweed (264), one of the most representative species of snowbeds in Iceland. These two species are usually found together, and only where snow cover is assured throughout winter. In districts with light snow cover, they are usually found from 350 m up to 800 or 1000 m. In very snow-heavy areas they are usually common all the way down to the seashore.

Leaf (1:1)

170 Northern Yellowcress
Rorippa islandica

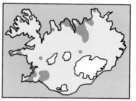

Flowers in short racemes, very small, 4-parted. Petals yellow, narrow, spatulate or ligulate, less than 2 mm long. Sepals shorter, pinkish to greenish purple, with membranous margin. Stamens six. Single pistil, about 1 mm long in flower. Fruit is a rotund, slightly curved silique, 7-10 mm long and 2-2.5 mm broad; the pedicel half the length of the fruit or less. Leaves 1-4 cm long, very variable in shape, pinnatifid or pinnate, esp. in lower part. Leaflets entire, dentate or lobed, the terminal leaflet usually larger than the others. **H:** 3-20 cm. **Hab:** Lake shores, bottom and margin of ponds which dry up in summer, damp river-beds. Rather rare except in N and SW Iceland. **Sim:** None. **Fl:** July. **I:** Kattarjurt. (Mustard family). — **Flixweed** *Descurainia sophia* is a very rare alien of the Mustard family, with very small, yellow flowers, and bi- or three-pinnate leaves with linear leaflets, resembling leaves of Mayweed.

Leaves (m. 1.5)

154

171 Hawkweed-leaved Treaclemustard
Erysimum hieraciifolium

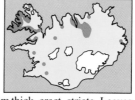

Flowers in racemes in leaf axils, 4-parted. Petals yellow, oblong, 7-9 mm long. Sepals green, 4-5 mm. Stamens six, single pistil. Fruit is a silique, 1.5-3 cm long and only 1 mm broad. Stem thick, erect, striate. Leaves alternate, lanceolate, 2-6 cm long, with sparse teeth and thinly covered with forked or stellate hairs. **H:** 40-70 cm. **Hab:** Dry slopes, cliffsides, roadsides, lake shores and islands. Rather rare except by Lake Mývatn, where it is quite common. **Sim:** No native species, but some aliens of the mustard family may be similar. **Fl:** July. **I:** Aronsvöndur. (Mustard family).

Leaf
(m. 1.3)

172 Winter-cress
Barbarea vulgaris

Flowers in racemes in leaf axils. Petals yellow, 4-7 mm long. Sepals only half as long, greenish, obtuse, with membranous margin. Stamens six. Single pistil, the fruit a 15-25 mm long, slender silique. Stem furrowed, glabrous, with alternate leaves. Upper stem-leaves coarsely dentate or lobed, sessile. Lower stem-leaves and basal leaves petioled, pinnate, with large, nearly round terminal leaflet, and one to three pairs of small lateral leaflets. **H:** 25-50 cm. **Hab:** Alien near houses and farms, in gardens and seeded homefields. Rather rare. **Sim:** Resembles some foreign aliens of the mustard family like the Carlock, not treated in this book. **Fl:** July. **I:** Garðableikja. (Mustard family).

Leaf
(r. 0.3)

173 Alpine Whitlowgrass
Draba alpina

Small plant with yellow, 4-parted flowers. Petals 3-4 mm long, obovate. Sepals 2 mm, elliptic with membranous margin. Stamens six. One pistil maturing to flat silicle, about 4-5 mm long and 2-3 mm broad. Stems hairy. Leaves elliptic to broadly lanceolate, entire, the margin hairy, a few forked hairs on both sides. **H:** 2-4 cm. **Hab:** Gravelly soil and rock outcrops at high altitudes. Rather rare. **Sim:** Resembles the Rock Whitlowgrass (131) when not in flower. The Alpine Whitlowgrass has shorter and broader silicles, and the leaf face is usually less hairy or not at all. **Fl:** July. **I:** Fjallavorblóm. (Mustard family). — The Alpine Whitlowgrass is one of the rarer plants of the high mountains, and prefers the more continental climate of the NE Central Highlands.

Open fruit
(m. 6)

174 Roseroot
■■
☐
Rhodiola rosea

Dioecious plant; flowers crowded in branched cluster or corymb terminally on upright branches of very thick rhizome. Petals ligulate, yellow, 3-5 mm long; sepals shorter. Male flowers (right) contain eight stamens, and four sterile pistils. Female flowers (left) bear 4-5 yellowish red pistils maturing to 7-10 mm long capsules, tipped with curved beak. Stem 2-6 mm thick, densely covered with ligulate or obovate leaves. Leaves usually pointed, often slightly dentate near tip, 2-4 cm long and 1-1.5 cm broad. Both stem and leaves glabrous. **H:** 10-30 cm. **Hab:** Since the Roseroot can not survive continuous grazing, it is usually found in steep cliffs, gorges or lake islands not accessible to sheep. Widespread. **Sim:** None. **Fl:** June. **I:** Burnirót. (Stonecrop family). — The Roseroot is very much favoured by sheep, and easily exterminated from pastures, except on inaccessible rock ledges. Where land has been protected from grazing, or has had moderate or discontinuous grazing for several decades, the roseroot may be found in fertile heathland and slopes. This applies to the Hornstrandir Nature Reserve, to Thjórsárver at the southern edge of Hofsjökull Glacier, and to Esjufjöll Mountains which are surrounded by the glacier Vatnajökull.

Fruit (m. 4)

175 Arctic Buttercup
☐☐
■
Ranunculus hyperboreus

Flowers 6-8 mm wide. Petals usually three, obovate. Sepals of same length or shorter, light-coloured. Stamens and pistils usually 10-15. Stem prostrate, usually with three-lobed, sometimes five-lobed, glabrous leaves. **H:** Completely prostrate. **Hab:** Mud, shallow ponds, lakes or springs. Rather common. **Sim:** Creeping Spearwort (see 167). The leaves resemble leaves of Brook Saxifrage (96). **Fl:** June. **I:** Sefbrúða. (Buttercup family). — The Arctic Buttercup is a species characteristic of iron-rich spring-water seeping up through mud in bogs, esp. in the Central Highlands. In these places it is usually accompanied by Water Whorlgrass (282).

Leaf (m. 2.5)

176 Lady's Bedstraw
Galium verum

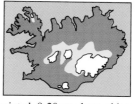

Flowers crowded in branched clusters in upper
leaf axils, 3-4 mm wide. Petals four, yellow,
pointed, fused at the base. Stamens four, one
pistil with divided style. Stems angular,
sparsely haired. Leaves 6-10 in whorls, linear, pointed, 8-20 mm long, shiny
on top, light green and pubescent underneath, margin revolute. **H:** 12-30 cm.
Hab: Dry, grassy plains, heaths and woodland. Common. **Sim:** None when
in flower. Before flowering the Lady's Bedstraw can be distinguished from
Northern Bedstraw (143) and Slender Bedstraw (144) by shape of leaves (see
drawings). **Fl:** June-July. **I:** Gulmaðra. (Madder family).

*Whorl of leaves
(m. 1.5)*

177 Meadow Vetchling
Lathyrus pratensis

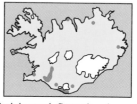

Flowers 1.5 cm long, zygomorphic, on short
pedicels, in six- to ten-flowered, one-sided
raceme. Petals yellow. Calyx 1 cm long, split
half way down into five, narrow, pointed seg-
ments; the veins hairy. Stamens ten, one pistil. Fruit is a pod. Stem sharply angular. Leaves alternate, pinnate, with one pair of foliage leaves and terminal
tendrils clasping neighbouring plants. Leaflets lanceolate, sharply pointed;
two obliquely arrow-shaped stipules at leaf base. **H:** 30-50 cm. **Hab:** Grassland and brushwood. Rather rare. **Sim:** None, easily recognized by the yellow, pea-like flowers and single pair of leaflets. **Fl:** July-August. **I:** Fugla-
ertur. (Pea family).

*Compound leaf
(r. 0.5)*

178 Small Cow-wheat
Melampyrum sylvaticum

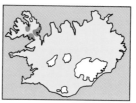

Flowers zygomorphic, solitary in leaf axils,
sessile. Corolla yellow, 10-13 cm long including tube; lower lip three-lobed, upper lip helmet-shaped with elevated keel, and recurved,
yellow-haired front margin. Calyx about 10 mm long, green, frequently with
purple stripe or spots, and four, revolute, acute segments. Stamens four; one
pistil maturing into a flat pod. Stems angular, hairy on two opposite sides.
Leaves opposite, lanceolate, 3-6 cm long, 8-10 mm broad; the margin revolute. **H:** 20-30 cm. **Hab:** Under birches in woodland. Rare. **Sim:** None. **Fl:**
July. **I:** Krossjurt. (Figwort family).

*Flower
(m. 2)*

160

179 Upright Lousewort
■□
□
Pedicularis flammea

Flowers 12-15 mm long in terminal raceme on stem. Corolla gamopetalous, zygomorphic, tubular, curved, with dark violet, laterally compressed, drooping helmet and yellow, three-lobed lower lip with round lobules. Calyx 6-9 mm long, with five short, denticulate lobes, green with violet lines or spots. Stamens four; single red-styled pistil. Stem angular or furrowed, dark, red, or tinged with blue. The leaves in basal rosette, oblong, stalked, pinnate, usually more or less violet-coloured; the leaflets crenate. **H:** 5-18 cm. **Hab:** Moist soil in mountain slopes, damp mossy bogs. Widespread in inland mountains, rare in coastal mountains. **Sim:** None. **Fl:** June. **I:** Tröllastakkur. (Figwort family).

Compound leaf (1:1)

180 Yellow-rattle
□■
□
Rhinanthus minor

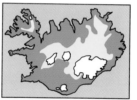

Flowers in upper leaf axils, zygomorphic, 15-18 mm long. Corolla gamopetalous with yellow helmet, usually with purple spot at the front. Calyx laterally compressed, 8-15 mm long, wide in centre with narrow opening, shortly incised. Stamens four. One pistil maturing into large, round and thin fruit, about 1 cm wide. Leaves opposite, oblong to lanceolate, sessile, 2-4 cm long and 0.5-1 cm broad, sometimes broader near base, with regular, sharp teeth, short-haired. **H:** 10-30 cm. **Hab:** Pastures and homefields, often in disturbed areas or in heathland. Common. **Sim:** None. **Fl:** June-July. **I:** Lokasjóður. (Figwort family). — The Yellow-rattle is often called Peningagras ("Penny-grass") by Icelandic children because of the shape of the fruits, which they use for play money.

Calyx (m. 2)

181 Kidney Vetch
□□
■
Anthyllis vulneraria

Many zygomorphic flowers in capitate, hairy heads subtended by oblong, green bracts. Petals yellow in upper part, 12-15 mm long. Calyx shorter, 5-lobed, hairy, for the most part whitish, but purple to reddish brown in upper part. Stamens ten, fused into tube around lower part of single, long pistil. Basal leaves odd-pinnate, stalked. Terminal leaflet obovate, larger than lateral leaflets, which are linear or absent. Stem-leaves sessile, their leaflets differing less in size. **H:** Procumbent branches 10-15 cm. **Hab:** Sandy or gravelly soil, dry unfertile grass plains or roadsides. Rather common in the Peninsula of Reykjanes up to the Mosfellssveit District, very rare elsewhere. **Sim:** None. **Fl:**June-July. **I:** Gullkollur. (Pea family).

Compound leaf (1:1)

182 Dandelion
Taraxacum spp.

Flowers densely packed in 3-5 cm wide heads which are solitary on top of unbranched, leafless, thick stem. Involucral bracts dark green, glabrous, usually with light or transparent margin; the upper bracts appressed to the head, the lower ones recurved. Florets all ligulate, the ligule 2-3 mm broad, bright yellow with five terminal teeth. Stamens five in each floret, fused into a tube around the style which has a divided stigma. Head closes after flowering and opens again when fruits are mature. Fruits ("seeds") are prickly on top, 2.5-5 mm long, with white pappus on long stalk that is two or three times the length of the fruit. Stem either tomentose or glabrous, 3-6 mm thick with wide central cavity. Leaves all in basal rosette, 15-30 cm long, very variable in shape, usually pinnately lobed or pinnatisect, with irregularly and coarsely toothed or lobed segments, rarely almost entire. Both stem and leaves contain white milky juice. **H:** 10-40 cm. **Hab:** Cultivated homefields and grassland, at the base of house walls, hollows in heathland, snowbeds in mountains. Very common. **Sim:** Easily distinguished from hawkweeds (183-185) and Autumn Hawkbit (186) by the unbranched, leafless stem with its wide cavity. **Fl:** April-June. **I:** Túnfífill. (Daisy family). — Dandelions are very variable plants and often separated into different numbers of microspecies. Since they reproduce by agamospermy, the distinction between many of the microspecies is unclear, and will not be treated further here.

Fruit
(m. 4.5)

183 Hawkweed
Hieracium spp.

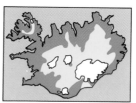

Flowers densely crowded in 2-3 cm broad heads, the single florets with bright yellow ligulate corolla. Stamens five, fused into a tube around the style which terminates in a bifid stigma. Involucral bracts greenish black, hairy, appressed. Stem often branched, finely haired, 1.5-2 mm broad, with one or more leaves; the other leaves basal, stalked, obovate, elliptic or lanceolate, coarsely dentate or lobed below, abrupt limits between blade and stalk. **H:** 25-40 cm. **Hab:** Vegetated slopes, hollows, heathland and brushwoods. Common. **Sim:** Hawkbit (186) and Dandelion (182). The Hawkweeds differ from both in usually having one or more stem-leaves. Hawk's-beard (see 186A). **Fl:** July-August. **I:** Undafífill. (Daisy family). — The hawkweeds are a very difficult group and have been divided by specialists into about 200 microspecies or varieties in Iceland. The description above fits some of the more common Icelandic hawkweeds. Other species can be rather different, some, for instance, have many stem-leaves. These microspecies will not be further treated here, except for the next species, Alpine Hawkweed, which differs from most other hawkweeds, and can be rather easily identified.

Fruit
(m. 3)

184 Alpine Hawkweed
■□
□
Hieracium alpinum

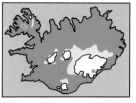

Flowers in dense, 2.5-3.5 cm wide heads. All
florets ligulate, bright yellow. Stamens five,
forming a tube around the style, which has a divided stigma. Involucral bracts greenish black,
hairy. Stem usually unbranched, rarely with one branch, dark, hairy, usually
with one leaf. Other leaves in basal rosette, the blade obovate, elliptic or lanceolate, slightly dentate, tapering to the stalk. **H:** 15-20 cm. **Hab:** Grassland,
hollows, grown mountain slopes or heathland. Common, esp. at higher altitudes. **Sim:** The Alpine Hawkweed is shorter and more hairy than most other
hawkweeds, and has a relatively larger flower head. **Fl:** June-July. **I:** Fella-
fífill. (Daisy family).

*Fruit
(m. 4.5)*

185 Icelandic Hawkweed
□■
□
Pilosella islandica

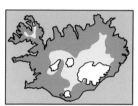

Flowers in 2-2.5 cm wide heads, with bright
yellow, ligulate florets. Stamens five, fused
into a tube around the style which has a bifid
stigma. Involucral bracts green, all appressed
with black midrib and long hairs. Stem branched below the top, with long (5-7
mm), stiff, black hairs. Leaves in basal rosette, about 8 cm long, lanceolate,
nearly entire, minutely denticulate with long marginal hairs. **H:** 20-35 cm.
Hab: Grassland, sheltered depressions and slopes. Common. **Sim:**
Hawkweeds (183-184). The Icelandic Hawkweed is best distinguished by the
very long, straight, black hairs on stem and leaves. Differs from Hawkbit
(186) and Dandelion (182) in the leaves. **Fl:** June-July. **I:** Íslandsfífill. (Daisy
family).

*Fruit
(m. 3.5)*

186 Autumn Hawkbit
□□
■
Leontodon autumnalis

Many flowers in dense, 2.5-3 cm wide heads.
All florets yellow, ligulate, 2-2.5 mm broad.
Stamens five, fused into a tube around the
style. Stigma bifid. Involucral bracts greenish
black, hairy, appressed. Stem branched, slender, 1.5-2 mm thick, striate.
Leaves in basal rosette, pinnately lobed, 5-15 cm long; the lobules usually
narrow. **H:** 15-30 cm. **Hab:** Homefields, grassy plains and slopes. Common.
Sim: Dandelions and hawkweeds (182-185). The Autumn Hawkbit is best
identified by the slender, branched stems, which are leafless except for a few
small bracts below the involucrum. Can also be distinguished by the bottom
of the head, which tapers gradually down to the stem. Other species have less
tapered bottom. **Fl:** July-August. **I:** Skarifífill. (Daisy family). — **Marsh
Hawk's-beard** *Crepis paludosa* is a tall (40-70 cm) perennial with many dentate leaves on the stem, with cordate, clasping base. The involucral bracts are
in two whorls. Very rare species, found only in the outer districts on both sides
of Eyjafjörður.

*Fruit
(m. 3.5)*

187 Colt's-foot
Tussilago farfara

Flower heads 2-3 cm wide with two types of florets. Rayflorets yellow with very thin (1/2 mm) ligulate corolla. Discflorets tubular with 5-lobed, 3 mm wide corolla. Stamens five, fused into a tube around the style, which has a bifid stigma. Involucral bracts in single, appressed whorl with green margin, brownish violet along the midrib and towards the tip. Stem tomentose, dense-leaved with appressed, broad-based, 1.5 cm long, brownish violet leaves. The Colt's-foot bears one head early in the spring, but basal leaves appear later. They are on long, 3-5 mm thick petiole; blade is cordate or reniform, irregularly dentate, 5-20 cm wide, glabrous on top, but white-tomentose underneath and on petioles. **H:** Stems and petioles 15-30 cm long. **Hab:** Waste places, dumps. Common in Reykjavík and its neighbourhood, rare elsewhere. **Sim:** None. Easily distinguished from dandelions and hawkweeds by the densely leafy stem, and the large, long-petioled leaves resembling Rhubarb. **Fl:** April-May. **I:** Hóffífill (Daisy family).

Fruit (m. 5)

188 Groundsel
Senecio vulgaris

Flowers in small, narrow (3-4 mm broad) heads. All florets tubular, yellow. Corolla 1 mm broad or less, 5-parted, 5-6 mm long. Pistil with divided stigma. Seeds with pappus. The inner involucral bracts long (8 mm), the outer much shorter, all appressed and black-tipped. Stem sparsely haired, with alternate leaves and few flower heads at the top. Leaves pinnately lobed, the lobules dentate. **H:** 12-25 cm. **Hab:** Vegetable gardens, roads, parking-lots, around houses. Common in densely populated areas. **Sim:** None. **Fl:** June-Sept. **I:** Krossfífill. (Daisy family).

Leaf (r. 0.6)

189 Pineappleweed
Chamomilla suaveolens

Many flowers in dense, globose heads, all tubular. Corolla greenish yellow. Involucral bracts broad, elliptic, green in centre with broad, membranous or three-pinnate, the leaflets linear. **Hab:** Unpaved roads, parking-lots, industrial and residential areas. Common in populated areas. **Sim:** Mayweed (74). The leaves very similar; the appleweed differ in the absence of the white rayflowers. **Fl:** July-Sept. **I:** Hlaðkolla. (Daisy family).

Leaf (r. 0.8)

190 Alpine Lady's-mantle
Alchemilla alpina

Many flowers clustered in leaf axils. Flowers 4-parted, 2.5-3.5 mm wide. Petals absent. Sepals yellowish green, four, arranged crosswise with tuft of hairs on the tip. Short, slender epicalyx lobes between sepals. Stamens four, single pistil with one style in lateral position. Leaves long-petioled (5-10 cm), palmate, with 5-7 leaflets. Leaflets 1.5-2 cm long, with toothed apex, densely silver-haired underneath, dark green and sparsely haired or glabrous on top. Quite thick rhizome with membranous, brown scale leaves. **H:** 5-15 cm. **Hab:** Depressions in slopes, snowbeds, screes, erosive soil. Common. **Sim:** Common Lady's-mantle (191). Only the flowers are similar, the leaves are different. **Fl:** June. **I:** Ljónslappi. (Rose family).

Leaf (1:1)

191 Common Lady's-mantle
Alchemilla vulgaris

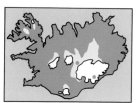

Flowers clustered in leaf axils, 3-4 mm wide, 4-parted. Petals absent. Sepals green or greenish yellow, arranged crosswise, acute, with terminal tuft of hair. Narrow epicalyx lobes between sepals, and half as long. Stamens four, single pistil with one lateral style. Basal leaves on long petiole (4-30 cm); the blade 4-10 cm wide, reniform, palmate-veined, with lobed margin; lobules regularly dentate. Differently haired according to subspecies. **H:** 15-40 cm. **Hab:** Dells and sheltered places in slopes, grassland, ravines. Common. **Sim:** Faeroeic Lady's-mantle (see 192). **Fl:** June. **I:** Maríustakkur. (Rose family). — The Common Lady's-mantle has been divided into several subspecies, sometimes treated as separate species, and some of them are rather easy to distinguish. The pictured Lady's-mantle (ssp. *filicaulis*) can be recognized by outstanding hairs on petioles. Pedicels also with outstanding hairs or glabrous. Ssp. *glomerulans* has appressed hairs on petioles and upper surface of leaves; the leaves are relatively large and usually lighter green. Reaches higher altitudes than the other subspecies. Ssp. *wichurae* also has appressed hairs on the petioles, but the upper surface of the leaves is glabrous, or with hairs only on the veins. It has slender and usually reddish pedicels. It is more restricted to warm locations than the other subspecies, and most common in S and W Iceland, esp. in sunny cliffs or slopes.

Leaf (r. 0.4)

192 Faeroeic Lady's-mantle

Alchemilla faeroënsis

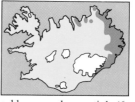

Flowers in dense clusters in leaf axils, 3-4 mm wide. Petals absent. Sepals four, yellowish green, acute, with terminal tuft of hairs, and short narrow epicalyx lobes in between. Stamens four, single pistil with one lateral style. Basal leaves on long petiole (6-10 cm). Blade 4-8 cm wide, palmately incised half way down or more, lobes 5-7, regularly dentate. Rhizome thick, 0.5-1 cm. **H:** 10-15 cm. **Hab:** Hollows and sheltered habitats in slopes, along creeks. Widespread in the East. **Sim:** Common Lady's-mantle (191). The Faeroeic Lady's-mantle differs in its more deeply incised leaves. **Fl:** June-July. **I:** Maríuvöttur. (Rose family). — The Faeroeic Lady's-mantle is one of the characteristic plants of E Iceland, although not as conspicuous as Pyramidal Saxifrage, Yellow Saxifrage and Harebell. Outside Iceland it is known only in the Faeroe Islands.

Leaf
(r. 0.5)

193 Procumbent Pearlwort

Sagina procumbens

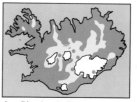

Flowers small, 2-2.5 mm wide. Petals usually absent, or at least much shorter than the sepals, white to transparent. Sepals four, rarely five, green, elliptic, about 2 mm long, with narrow, membranous margin. Stamens usually four to eight. Single pistil with four or five styles, maturing into an ovoid capsule. Sepals usually reflexed after capsule is mature. Leaves opposite, linear, sharp-pointed, 3-5 mm long, and 0.5 mm broad. **H:** 1.5-4 cm. **Hab:** Gravelly soil along brooks and rivers, sloping seashores, cold and warm springs, open soil in heathland. Common. **Sim:** Snow Pearlwort (see 140). Alpine Pearlwort (105). The Procumbent Pearlwort differs in the shorter pedicels, 4-parted flowers without petals, and usually reflexed sepals on the mature fruit. These last two species are difficult to identify before flowering, when both species have the sepals appressed to the bud. **Fl:** June-July. **I:** Skammkrækill. (Pink family).

Fruit in calyx
(m. 4.5)

194 Northern Green Orchid

Platanthera hyperborea

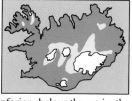

Flowers in long terminal spike. Perianth light green or yellowish green, bilabiate, with three perianth leaves forming upper lip, two lateral leaves pointing downwards and sideways, and one central leaf pointing straight down. Pistil inferior, below the perianth, striate and contorted. Seeds numerous, extremely small; curved spur extends down from perianth. Leaves alternate, lanceolate, tapering towards the tip, clasping the stem; the lower ones larger, 5-10 cm long and 10-18 mm broad. **H:** 15-30 cm. **Hab:** Fertile heathland, grassy slopes. Common. **Sim:** Small-white Orchid (195). The Northern Green Orchid differs in the central perianth leaf of the lower lip, which is entire; the inflorescence is also coarser than on the Small-white Orchid. **Fl:** June. **I:** Friggjargras. (Orchid family).

Flower (m. 3)

195 Small-white Orchid
Pseudorchis albida

Flowers in terminal spike. Perianth yellowish green to whitish, six-leaved, bilabiate. Lower lip formed by single, three-lobed perianth leaf; upper lip consists of the rest of the leaves, which are all entire, elliptic or lanceolate. Pistil inferior, below the perianth, green, contorted. Curved spur extends down from the perianth. Stem leafy, 2-5 mm thick. Leaves alternate, lanceolate, 3-8 cm long and 1-2 cm broad, entire, parallel-veined. Numerous extremely small seeds. **H:** 15-25 cm. **Hab:** Grassy heathland, sheltered, fertile slopes. Rather common. **Sim:** Northern Green Orchid (194). The Small-white Orchid differs in the three-lobed leaf of the lower lip, smaller flowers and more delicate inflorescence; the leaves relatively broader and the upper side glossy. **Fl:** June. **I:** Hjónagras. (Orchid family).

Flower (m. 4)

196 Herb-Paris

Paris quadrifolia

Upright side branches rise from horizontal rhizome, each with four leaves in a whorl near the top, terminating in one, four-parted flower. Sepals lanceolate, narrow-pointed, green, 2-3 cm long and 4-5 mm broad. Inner perianth leaves shorter, yellowish green, linear. Stamens eight with long, yellow anthers. Pistil dark violet, maturing to a still darker, poisonous berry. Leaves elliptic-obovate, 5-8 cm long and 3-4 cm broad in full size, with parallel, curved veins, almost entire. **H:** 15-35 cm. **Hab:** Brushwood and lava fissures. Rare. **Sim:** None. **Fl:** July. **I:** Ferlaufungur. (Birth Root family).

Fruit (m. 2.8)

197 Various-leaved Pondweed

Potamogeton gramineus

Aquatic plant with elliptic, floating leaves on long, slender petioles. Blade 2-6 cm long and 1 cm broad. Submerged leaves lanceolate, acute, sessile, usually 3-6 cm long and 0.5 cm broad.

Stipules membranous, linear, 1-2 cm long. Flowers small, in 1.5-2 cm long, greenish or light brown spike just above water surface. Perianth absent; four stamens and pistils. Stem thicker just below spike. **H:** 10-40 cm, depending on depth of water. **Hab:** Shallow pools and lakes, marshland, sometimes in flooded bogs along with sedges. **Sim:** Red Pondweed (198). The Various-leaved Pondweed differs in the sharp-pointed submerged leaves, and the thickening of the stem below the spike. The floating leaves recall those of Broad-leaved Pondweed (199), but are smaller and thinner; the Various-leaved Pondweed can be distinguished by the submerged leaves which are lacking on Broad-leaved Pondweed. **Fl:** July-August. **I:** Grasnykra. (Pondweed family).

Floating leaf (r. 0.6)

198 Red Pondweed

Potamogeton alpinus

Aquatic plant, usually submerged except for flowers, rarely with floating leaves. Floating leaves lanceolate, 5-10 cm long, the blade tapering gradually to the petiole. Submerged

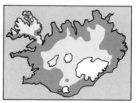

leaves long, usually 6-16 cm, tapering gradually to base, but stalkless, with blunt, brown or greenish tip. Flowers small, in 1.5-2.5 cm long spike standing out of the water, with four stamens and pistils. Stem not thicker below spike. **H:** 20-60 cm. **Hab:** Ponds and lakes, sometimes up to 4-500 m. Common. **Sim:** Various-leaved Pondweed (197). The Red Pondweed differs through the long, obtuse submerged leaves. Long-stalked Pondweed (201). The Red Pondweed differs through the submerged leaves tapering towards the base. **Fl:** July. **I:** Fjallnykra. (Pondweed family).

Submerged leaf (r. 0.3)

199 Broad-leaved Pondweed

Potamogeton natans

Aquatic plant with elliptic, 4-9 cm long and 1.5-3 cm broad floating leaves with parallel, curved veins, sharp midrib and usually very long petiole. No submerged leaves; leaves

below water surface are bladeless stalks. Flowers small, on 1.5-3.5 cm long, greenish or tawny spike which protrudes through water surface; four stamens and pistils. **H:** 30-100 cm depending on depth of water. **Hab:** Lakes and deep ponds or larger drainage ditches. Rather rare. **Sim:** Various-leaved Pondweed (197). The Broad-leaved Pondweed differs in that submerged leaves are absent or bladeless. **Fl:** July-August. **I:** Blöðkunykra. (Pondweed family).

Floating leaf (r. 0.3)

200 Perfoliate Pondweed
Potamogeton perfoliatus

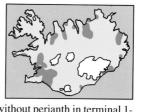

Leaves relatively short and broad (3-6 x 1.5-2.5 cm), obovate to elliptic, dark green, broad towards base, densely arranged and sessile, clasping the stem, extremely finely denticulate, with curved nerves. Many, very small flowers without perianth in terminal 1-2 cm long and 5 mm broad spike protruding through water surface. Four stamens with small, greenish brown lobes resembling perianth. Pistils four. **H:** 30-100 cm. **Hab:** Small and large lakes, preferring those warmed through the sun, or containing thermal water; thermal streams. Rather rare. **Sim:** Long-stalked Pondweed (201). The Perfoliate Pondweed can be distinguished by the leaves being only two or three times as long as broad, while those of Long-stalked Pondweed are 7-10 times longer than broad. **Fl:** July-August. **I:** Hjartanykra. (Pondweed family).

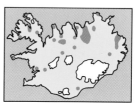

*Leaf
(r. 0.8)*

201 Long-stalked Pondweed
Potamogeton praelongus

Leaves long (10-20 cm), broader towards base (1-2.5 cm), sessile and partly clasping stem; leaf margin very finely denticulate or entire. Stipules membranous, 4-7 cm long, greyish brown. Flowers small, without perianth, many in terminal spike, which may be as long as 4 cm; the stalk not thicker below spike than further down. Stamens four with greenish brown appendages resembling perianth. Pistils four. **H:** 50-300 cm. **Hab:** Deep ponds and lakes. Rather rare. **Sim:** Red Pondweed (198). The Long-stalked Pondweed differs through broad base of leaves. Perfoliate Pondweed (see 200). **Fl:** July-August. **I:** Langnykra. (Pondweed family).

*Leaf
(r. 0.2)*

202 Slender-leaved Pondweed
Potamogeton filiformis

Leaves filiform, with sheathing base, usually 15-20 cm long and 1 mm broad, submerged or floating. Flowers several together in three to five capitate clusters at 0.5-1 cm intervals on stem, usually floating on water surface. Stamens four with greenish tawny, round appendages resembling perianth. Anthers light-coloured, 1 mm broad. Pistils four. **H:** 15-50 cm, shorter on periodically flooded mud flats, and longer (1-2m) in running water, as in the river Laxá near Mývatn. **Hab:** Shallow lakes and ponds, stream beds and flooded mud flats. Common; occurs at higher altitudes than other pondweeds. **Sim:** Lesser Pondweed (203) and Horned Pondweed (204). The Slender-leaved Pondweed has much longer leaves, and is easily distinguished in flower by regular intervals between flower knots. **Fl:** June-July. **I:** Þráðnykra. (Pondweed family).

*Inflorescence
(m. 1.5)*

203 Lesser Pondweed

Potamogeton pusillus

Leaves linear, 2.5-4 cm long and 1-1.5 mm broad, obtuse or with short terminal point, no sheaths at base, usually submerged. Stipules membranous, narrow, 4-8 mm long. Flowers 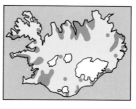 several together in short (5-7 mm), nearly round spike on end of stem, floating on water surface or submerged. **H:** 10-25 cm. **Hab:** Shallow lakes or ponds. Rather widespread. **Sim:** Slender-leaved Pondweed (see 202). Horned Pondweed (204). The Lesser Pondweed differs from Horned Pondweed by the terminal flower spike. **Fl:** June-July. **I:** Smánykra. (Pondweed family).

Inflorescence (m. 2.2)

204 Horned Pondweed

Zannichellia palustris

Delicate, repeatedly branched aquatic plant. Leaves opposite or in whorls of three, 1.5-4 cm long, filiform (0.3 mm thick), with membranous sheaths. Flowers in leaf axils, unisexual, 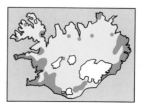 usually one male and one female flower in each whorl. Female flowers with 3-5 pistils maturing into curved, beaked fruits 2-3 mm long. **H:** 15-30 cm. **Hab:** Shallow ditches or slow-streaming water in the lowland, frequently in rills flooded with brackish water at high tide. Rare. **Sim:** Slender-leaved Pondweed (see 202). Lesser Pondweed (see 203). The Horned Pondweed can best be distinguished by the curved fruits in the leaf axils. **Fl:** July. **I:** Hnotsörvi. (Horned Pondweed family). — **Beaked Tasselweed** *Ruppia maritima* is a very rare, delicate plant with branched stems and filiform, fine leaves. Occurs in lagoons with brackish water. Flowers without perianth on long pedicels, winding spirally when fruits mature.

Fruit (m. 4.5)

205 Bulbous Rush

Juncus bulbosus

Perennial plant of very different habits depending on whether growing in moist soil or submerged in water. When submerged it forms dense tufts of long (10-20 cm), filiform leaves (0.1-0.5 mm), flowers often imperfect and sometimes viviparous. When growing in mud out of water, it will have shorter and thicker leaves (0.5-1.5 mm), usually reddish. Flower clusters are then more regular with 3-7 flowers. Perianth leaves six, red or green, with transparent or brownish membranous margin, pointed. Stamens three, single pistil with trifid stigma. Fruit truncate with short terminal point. Often forming small bulblike swellings in basal leaf sheaths. **H:** 5-30 cm depending on depth of water. **Hab:** Mud along pondsides or lakes, or submerged on the bottom. Fairly widespread, but rare in the North. **Sim:** None. **Fl:** July. **I:** Hnúðsef. (Rush family).

Fruit in calyx (m. 7)

206 Eelgrass
Zostera marina

Marine plant with alternate, dark green, linear, 2-4 mm broad, parallel-veined leaves with undulate margin and rounded tip. Two rows of flowers in a spike enclosed within the sheath of the leaves. Flowers without perianth; single stamen and pistil in each flower. **H:** 30-100 cm. **Hab:** Shallow water with mud bottom, calm coves and fjords, either entirely submerged in the sea or exposed at low tide. Rather widespread. **Sim:** Bur-reeds (207-208) have similar leaves, but are never found in the sea, and the inflorescence is different. **Fl:** August-October. **I:** Marhálmur. (Eel-grass family).

Fruit (m. 6)

207 Northern Bur-reed
Sparganium hyperboreum

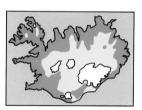

Leaves flat, linear, 5-30 cm long. The lower leaves longer than the upper, 2-3 mm broad, with the upper end floating. Flowers unisexual in capitate heads on water surface or rising slightly above the water. Male flowers in uppermost heads, which are perishable. Female flowers in the lower, usually two or three. Perianth leaves membranous, brownish, inconspicuous. Three stamens in each male flower. Pistils of female heads mature into ovoid, 2 mm long fruits. Fruits crowded in compact, ca. 1 cm wide globose head. **H:** 20-50 cm. **Hab:** Ponds and peat-pits or small lakes. Common. **Sim:** Least Bur-reed (see 207A). Floating Bur-reed (208). The Northern Bur-reed has smaller heads than the Floating Bur-reed, and shorter, beakless fruits. **Fl:** June-July. **I:** Mógrafabrúsi. (Bur-reed family). — **Least Bur-reed** *Sparganium minimum* is closely related to Northern Bur-reed, and not easy to distinguish. They differ mainly through the fruit which is short-beaked on Least Bur-reed, but unbeaked on Northern Bur-reed.

Fruit (m. 8.5)

208 Floating Bur-reed
■☐
☐
Sparganium angustifolium

Leaves flat, linear, 6-50 cm long, the lower longer and 2-5 mm broad, the upper shorter, 6-10 mm broad at the base. Flowers in capitate heads rising up above the water surface, male flowers in upper heads, female in two or three lower heads; the lowest one on long stalk. Perianth leaves membranous, brownish. Three stamens in each male flower. Pistils of female flowers mature into ovoid, 3-5 mm long, distinctly beaked fruit. Mature fruit heads 1-1.5 cm wide. **H:** 30-75 cm. **Hab:** Ponds and small lakes. Rather rare. **Sim:** Least and Northern Bur-reed (see 207). **Fl:** July. **I:** Trjónubrúsi. (Bur-reed family).

Fruit
(m. 7)

209 Spring Quillwort
☐■
☐
Isoëtes echinospora

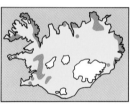

Submerged water plant with dense tuft of erect, strict, linear, acute, green or brownish leaves, with light-coloured, broader base. Sporangia enclosed within the leaf base, those of outer leaves containing echinulate, globose macrospores, those of inner leaves enclosing great number of minute, elongated microspores. Leaves rise from 5-15 mm broad, short, disclike stem. **H:** 4-8 cm. **Hab:** Shallow or deep ponds, small lakes, occurs from shore-line to a depth of 2-3 m. **Sim:** Quillwort (see 209A). Awlwort (see 137). Shoreweed (210) produces similar tufts of leaves. The Spring Quillwort differs through the sporangia within the leaf base, and the four air canals inside the leaves, visible in section. **I:** Álftalaukur. (Quillwort family). — **Quillwort** *Isoëtes lacustris* is very similar and closely related. It has longer leaves with a broader tip. The surface of the spores should be examined for identification; it is reticulate on Quillwort and echinulate on Spring Quillwort.

Spore
(m. 70)
and leaf section
(m. 10)

210 Shoreweed
☐☐
■
Littorella uniflora

Leaves arranged in dense basal tufts, linear, elliptic in section, 5-10 cm long and 1-2 mm broad, occasionally forming short, curved, rooting runners. Flowers unisexual, monoecious. Male flowers stand out on long pedicels, 4-parted. Sepals green or red-striped with membranous margin, pointed, 4-5 mm long. Petals longer, pointed, with membranous margin. Stamens of male flowers 1-2 cm long, protruding far out of the flower. Anthers large, 2-3 mm long. Female flowers sessile in axils of bracts at base of male flowers. One, single-styled pistil. Fruit a 2-2.5 mm long, one-seeded nut. **H:** 5-10 cm. **Hab:** Ponds, lake-beds and inlets from lakes, sometimes forming continuous, bright green cover on lake bottoms. Widespread in the Southwest, rare elsewhere. **Sim:** Quillwort and Spring Quillwort (see 209). **Fl:** July. **I:** Tjarnalaukur. (Plantain family).

Leaf section
(m. 10)

211 Alternate Water-milfoil
Myriophyllum alterniflorum

Aquatic plant, rooted in the bottom and sub-merged with the exception of flower spikes. Flowers small, unisexual, in loose, terminal spike. Perianth 4-parted, with calyx and corolla. Petals white or reddish. Stamens eight, one pistil. Leaves usually four in a whorl, pinnate with filiform lobes, 1.5-2 cm long. **H:** 25-50 cm. **Hab:** Slow streaming dykes, ponds and lakes. Common. **Sim:** Spiked Water-mil-foil (see 211A). Leaves recall Thread-leaved Water-crowfoot (92), but differ in being clearly pinnate. **Fl:** July. **I:** Síkjamari. (Water-milfoil family). — **Spiked Water-milfoil** *Myriophyllum spicatum* resembles Alternate Water-milfoil, but is rare. It has longer and more coarsely divided leaves, 1.2-3 cm; the lower part of the stem has characteristic, appressed and downwards-oriented leaves, but on Alternate Water-milfoil the stems are usually leafless in the lower part.

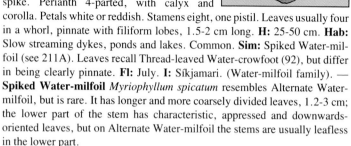

Submerged leaf (m. 1.8)

212 Lesser Bladderwort
Utricularia minor

Rootless water plant, floating submerged in the water. Rarely flowers in Iceland. Flower stem erect with few, yellow, gamopetalous flowers. Corolla bilabiate, 7-10 mm long, spurred; the throat narrow. Leaf shoots branched, leaves finely divided with pointed, linear segments. Leaves carry one or more small (1.5-2 mm) hunting bladders with opening closed by a small flap. Since under-pressure is maintained, small animals are sucked into the bladder when the flap opens by their move-ment against stiff hairs on the outside. The animals are thus captured and di-gested. Plant often forms fairly extensive tangles in the water. **H:** Submerged shoots, usually 10-20 cm or longer. **Hab:** Peat-pits, calm ditches, pools or small ponds in marshland. Rather rare. **Sim:** None; the bladders are quite dis-tinctive. **Fl:** August. **I:** Blöðrujurt. (Bladderwort family).

Hunting bladder (m. 10)

213 Vernal Water-starwort
Callitriche palustris

Leaves of two different types. Submerged leaves opposite, linear, 7-10 mm long, 0.5-1 mm broad, with indented tip. Floating leaves with broad (2 mm), blunt tip, forming terminal rosette on water surface. Flowers solitary in leaf axils, sessile, unisexual, without perianth. Male flowers with only one stamen. Female flowers with one, two-styled pistil. Fruit greenish brown, obovate or obcordate, slightly elongated. **H:** 10-30 cm. **Hab:** Mud in or around pools and creeks, submerged or exposed. Rather common. **Sim:** Hooktipped Water-starwort (see 214). Common Water-starwort (see 215). **Fl:** June-July. **I:** Vorbrúða. (Starwort family).

Floating leaf and submerged leaf (m. 4.5)

214 Hooktipped Water-starwort
Callitriche hamulata

Leaves of two different types. Submerged leaves opposite, linear, narrow, 1-2.5 cm long and 0.3-0.5 mm broad, with two extremely fine hooks at the tip. Floating leaves 5-8 mm long, broadest in the upper part, with indented tip, forming terminal rosettes on shoots reaching the water surface. Flowers solitary in leaf axils, without perianth, sessile; male flowers with one stamen, the female ones with single pistil. Fruit blackish green, nearly round, 1.5 mm wide. **H:** 15-50 cm. **Hab:** Pools, slow-flowing streams or ponds, often completely submerged. Common. **Sim:** Vernal Water-starwort (213). The Hooktipped Water-starwort differs through longer submerged leaves, terminal claws, and indented or truncate floating leaves. **Fl:** June-July. **I:** Síkjabrúða. (Starwort family). — **Penduncled Water-starwort** *Callitriche brutia* is very rare in Iceland, in most ways resembling Vernal Water-starwort or Hooktipped Water-starwort, except that the flowers and fruits have distinct, short pedicels. The leaves are not as long as on Hooktipped Starwort, but have similar terminal teeth.

Floating leaf and submerged leaf (m. 4.5)

215 Common Water-starwort
Callitriche stagnalis

Submerged leaves opposite, linear or spatulate; floating leaves in rosettes, rather broad (2-4 mm) with rounded end and usually clearly three-veined. Flowers unisexual; male flowers with one stamen, female flowers with single, two-styled pistil. Fruit greenish brown with narrow membranous wing at the margin, 1.2-1.5 mm, with short, erect, persistent styles. **H:** 10-30 cm depending on depth of water. **Hab:** Warm springs and their outlets, mud in shallow water and ditches. Widespread in the South, elsewhere usually restricted to thermal soil. **Sim:** Vernal Water-starwort (213) and Hooktipped Water-starwort (214). The Common Water-starwort differs through broader, more roundish, three-veined leaves in floating rosettes. **Fl:** July. **I:** Laugabrúða. (Starwort family). — **Autumn Water-starwort** *Callitriche hermaphroditica* is a rather rare species with a dense-leaved stem. The leaves are decussate, relatively short (5-10 mm), with indented tip and broad base, floating rosette absent. Totally submerged in water at the bottom of ponds or streams, differs distinctly from other starworts.

Floating leaf (m. 5)

216 Mare's-tail
Hippuris vulgaris

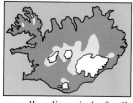

Rather coarse aquatic plant with 2-3 mm thick stems, standing mostly out of the water. Leaves in whorls, usually 8-12 on each node, linear or lanceolate, 1-1.5 cm long. Submerged stems with longer, softer leaves, 2-3 cm. Flowers very small, solitary in leaf axils and forming whorl around the stem, bisexual, epigynous. Perianth simple, forming four short appendages near top of pistil. Only one pistil and one stamen in each flower. **H:** 20-60 cm depending on depth of water. **Hab:** Ponds and lake inlets, flooded marshland, occasionally in streams or deep watercourses cut into peatland. Common. **Sim:** Four-leaved Mare's-tail (see 216A). **Fl:** July. **I:** Lófótur. (Mare's-tail family). — **Four-leaved Mare's-tail** *Hippuris tetraphylla* resembles the Common Mare's-tail, and is by some specialists regarded as a variety of that species. It is shorter (10-40 cm), with broader leaves (2-5 mm) only four to six in a whorl. The Four-leaved Mare's-tail is restricted to muddy salt marshes and ditches with brackish water.

Flower (m. 10)

217 Water Horsetail
Equisetum fluviatile

Stems jointed, round, with wide central cavity, branchless or with few, short, round branches. Each node has a sheath with 12-14 dark brown or black, sharply pointed teeth, usually with light brown zone below the teeth. All stems green, fertile stems terminating in blackish cone of sporangial leaves, blunt-tipped. **H:** 30-80 cm, in deep water still longer. **Hab:** Ponds, lakes, ditches, calm water courses, marshland and bogs. Common. **Sim:** Rough Horsetail (223). The Water Horsetail is softer, with a wider central cavity, more regular and persistent teeth, and grows in wetter habitats. **I:** Fergin. (Horsetail family).

Stem sheath (m. 2.2)

218 Marsh Horsetail
Equisetum palustre

Stems jointed, round, furrowed, with whorls of jointed branches. Toothed sheath on every node; teeth 6-8, brown, with membranous margin near tip. Branches often rather sparse, usually short, dull-angled with 5-6 furrows and same number of brown-tipped teeth. All stems green, the fertile ones tipped with greenish black sporangial cone. **H:** 20-40 cm. **Hab:** Peat bogs and mires. Common. **Sim:** Variegated Horsetail (see 222). Field Horsetail (219). The Marsh Horsetail differs through softer and greater number of angles on branches, fewer branches, and through green colour of fertile shoots. **I:** Mýrelfting. (Horsetail family).

Stem sheath with lateral branch (m. 3.5)

219 Field Horsetail

Equisetum arvense

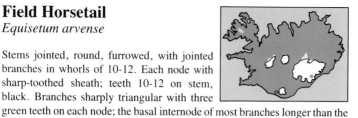

Stems jointed, round, furrowed, with jointed branches in whorls of 10-12. Each node with sharp-toothed sheath; teeth 10-12 on stem, black. Branches sharply triangular with three green teeth on each node; the basal internode of most branches longer than the stem sheath, often with exception of lowest branches. Sporangial cones appear quite early in spring, on light brown, unbranched stems with black sheaths. These fertile shoots wither again after the spores have been dispersed. **H:** 20-40 cm; prostrate varieties are also common in Iceland. **Hab:** Gardens, waste places, roadsides, heathland and as undergrowth in woodland. Very common. **Sim:** Wood Horsetail (see 221). Shady Horsetail (220). The Field Horsetail has coarser, more upright branches than the Shady Horsetail. The relation between the lowest branch internode and adjoining stem sheath is also an identifying characteristic if examined around central part of stem. Marsh Horsetail (218). The Field Horsetail differs through more numerous, triangular branches. **I:** Klóelfting. (Horsetail family).

Stem sheath with lateral branch (1:1)

220 Shady Horsetail

Equisetum pratense

Stems round, jointed, furrowed, finely verruculose, with jointed branches in whorls of 10-16. Sharp-toothed sheath on each node, teeth 10-16, with broad, white, membranous margin, black in centre; the sheath green below the teeth. Branches almost horizontal or slightly curved downwards, sharply triangular, three-dentate, unbranched. Lowest internode of branches shorter than corresponding stem sheath if checked in centre part of the stem or further down. Sporangial cones mature early in summer on unbranched stems which become green and branched after spores are shed. **H:** 15-25 cm. **Hab:** Dry pastures and heathland, also as undergrowth in woodland. Common. **Sim:** Field Horsetail (see 219). **I:** Vallelfting. (Horsetail family).

Stem sheath with lateral branch (1:1)

221 Wood Horsetail
Equisetum sylvaticum

Stems round, jointed, furrowed, with jointed branches in whorls of 9-12. Dentate sheath on every node, teeth brown or reddish brown above. Branches sharply quadrangular with greenish or brownish teeth, the branches themselves again divided into two or three branches at lower nodes; upper part of branches triangular with unbranched nodes. **H:** 20-40 cm. **Hab:** Woodland and copses. Very rare. **Sim:** Rather easily distinguished by the brownish sheaths and the divided branches. **I:** Skógelfting. (Horsetail family).

Stem sheath with lateral branch (1:1)

222 Variegated Horsetail
Equisetum variegatum

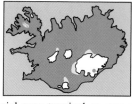

Stems slender, jointed, five- to eight-angled, unbranched or slightly branched near base, rigid, evergreen. Dentate sheath at every node; teeth 5-8, black in centre, with broad membranous margin; black zone below teeth. Sporangial cone terminal on green stems, black or brown, pointed. **H:** 15-25 cm. **Hab:** Wide variety of habitats, heathland, screes, dry slopes, sandy soils, moist soil and bogs, both near the seashore and in the mountains. Common. **Sim:** Rough Horsetail (223). The Variegated Horsetail differs by its much more slender stems, with narrower central cavity; also by fewer and more persistent teeth on stem sheath. Marsh Horsetail (218) can be difficult to distinguish from Variegated Horsetail in bogs; the Marsh Horsetail is more branched and the cone is not pointed. **I:** Beitieski. (Horsetail family).

Stem sheath (m. 3)

223 Rough Horsetail
Equisetum hyemale

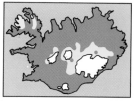

Stems are thick, 4-5 mm, jointed, rigid, unbranched or with few basal branches, evergreen. Dentate sheath at every node, light grey with narrow, black zone at base. Teeth on sheath 18-20, evanescent, the margin becoming irregular or ravelled. Sporangial cone terminal, black, pointed. **H:** 20-30 cm. **Hab:** Widespread in heathland, gravelly slopes, screes or woodland. **Sim:** Variegated Horsetail (see 222). Water Horsetail (see 217). **I:** Eski. (Horsetail family).

Stem sheath (m. 2)

224 Common Polypody
Polypodium vulgare

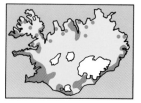

Leaves rise from strong, horizontal rhizome, pinnatifid, with 6-12 nearly entire or finely crenulate, obtuse lobes on each side. Lobes 1.5-2.5 cm long, 4-7 mm broad, gradually shorter towards tip of blade, longest at the base. The lower side with two rows of large sori and sharp, delicate midrib. Indusium absent. **H:** 6-25 cm, whereof more than half consists of the blade, and the rest is the stalk. **Hab:** Rock crevices and cliff walls. Widespread in the South and West, rare in the North. **Sim:** None. **I:** Köldugras. (Polypody family).

Sori on lower side of leaf (r. 0.6)

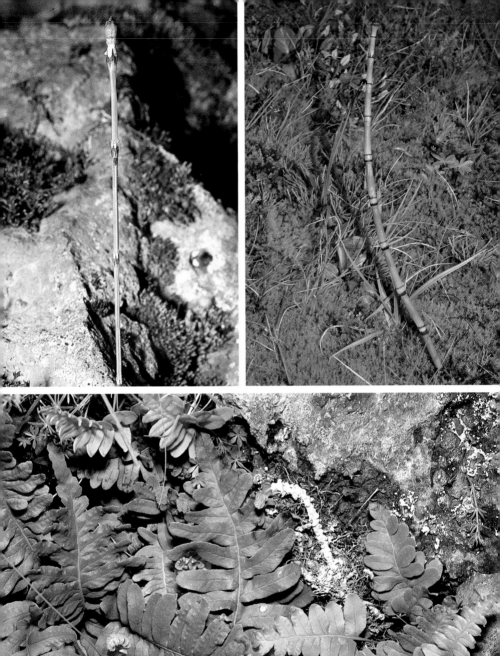

225 Hard Fern
Blechnum spicant

Leaves rise from horizontal rhizome, evergreen, pinnatifid or deeply incised, with 30-45 entire, slightly pointed pinnules on each side. Pinnules 1-2 cm long and 2-4 mm broad, the longest ones in the centre. Fertile leaves quite different: erect, pinnate, shaped like a two-sided comb, their pinnules quite narrow (1 mm), the sori forming a continuous line on the lower side. Fertile leaves are not always present. **H:** 15-35 cm, whereof only 1/5 to 1/4 is the stalk; stalk of fertile leaves may be as much as half of the total leaf length. **Hab:** Snowbeds and ravines, usually not above 400 m. Rather rare. **Sim:** Holly Fern (see 226). **I:** Skollakambur (Hardfern family). — The Hard Fern generally occurs only in snowbeds in districts with heavy snowfalls in the lowland. The only exception is a variety (var. *fallax*) growing in thermal areas. These plants are smaller, the sterile and fertile leaves both of same type.

*Part of leaf
(m. 1.2)*

226 Holly Fern
Polystichum lonchitis

Leaves grow from thick, horizontal rhizome, evergreen, pinnate, with 20-40 sharply dentate, obliquely rhomboid, 1-1.5 cm long leaflets, the longest near centre of blade. Leaves all alike, sori in two rows on underside of leaflets. Indusium covers young sori. **H:** 12-30 cm. **Hab:** Snowbeds, hollows and ravines. Widespread except in the South. **Sim:** Hard Fern (225). The Holly Fern is easily distinguished by the dentate leaflets. **I:** Skjaldburkni. (Fern family). — The Holly Fern grows in snowbeds like the Hard Fern, but is less dependent on the snow cover and therefore more widespread.

*Part of leaf
(1:1)*

227 Green Spleenwort
Asplenium viride

Small fern with pinnate leaves. Blade 4-10 cm long and 7-12 mm broad. Leaflets obliquely rhomboid, ovate or nearly round, crenate; two to five small sori on lower side of leaflets. Membranous indusium present next to youngest sori, not persistent. Petioles brown in lower part, green in upper part; midrid of blade also green. **H:** 8-12 cm. **Hab:** Rock crevices, esp. in rocky walls facing south. Very rare. **Sim:** Maidenhair Spleenwort (228). The Green Spleenwort is best distinguished by green midrib of blade (black or dark brown on Maidenhair Spleenwort). Alpine Woodsia (see 232). **I:** Klettaburkni. (Spleenwort family). — Until recently the Green Spleenwort was only known in few localities in SE Iceland, but has now also been discovered in the North. Some of these were buried in lava from the Leirhnjúkur eruption.

Lateral leaflet with sori (m. 4)

228 Maidenhair Spleenwort
Asplenium trichomanes

Small fern with pinnate leaves. Blade 5-10 cm long, 7-12 mm broad. Leaflets ovate, dentate, 4-5 mm long. Sori small, 4-8 on each leaflet. Indusium next to sorus, membranous, persistent. Petiole and midrib dark brown or nearly black. **H:** 8-16 cm. **Hab:** Rock crevices. Very rare. **Sim:** Green Spleenwort (see 227). **I:** Svartburkni. (Spleenwort family). — **Forked Spleenwort** *Asplenium septentrionale* has been found only in one rock crevice in the North. It looks quite different from other spleenworts. It has dissected leaves, with few, linear lobes. The sori cover the whole lower surface of the lobes.

Lateral leaflet with sori (m. 4)

229 Common Moonwort
Botrychium lunaria

Very short, vertical rhizome with one upright leaf divided into fertile branch with cluster of sporangia, and sterile branch with 2-6 cm long, pinnate blade with moon- or fan-shaped leaflets. Leaflets 0.5-1 cm long, 1-1.5 cm broad, with wavy or entire margin. Sporangial cluster repeatedly branched; sporangia globose, opening by slit through apex. **H:** 8-20 cm. **Hab:** Grassy hollows and slopes or flat pastures. Common. **Sim:** Northern Moonwort (230) and Lance-leaved Moonwort (231). The Common Moonwort is easily distinguished by the shape of the leaflets. **I:** Tungljurt. (Adder's-tongue family). — **Glossy Moonwort** *Botrychium simplex* is a small, rare species. It differs from other moonworts in basal attachment of the blade; blade is also less compound, either lobed or with only one pair of leaflets. The fertile branch on very long stalk.

Lateral leaflet (m. 1.5)

230 Northern Moonwort
Botrychium boreale

Very short, upright, single-leaved rhizome, the leaf divided in the upper part into fertile branch with cluster of sporangia, and sterile branch with pinnate blade. Blade 2-5 cm long, with rhomboid, incised leaflets with blunt lobes; the lowest ones 1-1.5 cm long and equally wide. Sporangia globose, 1 mm wide, opening by a slit through the apex. **H:** 6-15 cm. **Hab:** Grassland and grassy heath or slopes. Rare. **Sim:** Lance-leaved Moonwort (see 231). **I:** Mánajurt. (Adder's-tongue family).

Lateral leaflet (m. 2.3)

231 Lance-leaved Moonwort
Botrychium lanceolatum

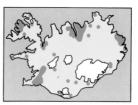

Very short, upright, single-leaved rhizome. Leaf divided in upper part into two parts: a branched cluster of sporangia, and a pinnate blade. Blade 1-2.5 cm long with pinnately lobed leaflets; the longest 1-1.5 cm long and 5-8 mm broad, with four incisions on each side. Sporangial cluster repeatedly branched, sporangia globose, opening by a slit through the apex. **H:** 5-10 cm. **Hab:** Flat grassland or dry, grassy slopes. Rather rare. **Sim:** Northern Moonwort (230). The Lance-leaved Moonwort differs in longer, more regular pinnately lobed leaflets. These two species are not always easy to tell apart. **I:** Lensutungljurt. (Adder's-tongue family).

Lateral leaflet (m. 1.5)

232 Oblong Woodsia
Woodsia ilvensis.

Leaves upright on stout, horizontal rhizome, 6-12 cm long, pinnate. Leaflets pinnately lobed or pinnatifid, 0.5-1.5 cm long, the lower side covered with oblong, small, membranous scales and hairs, esp. along veins. Sori in two rows; indusium split into narrow segments, terminating in long hairs. Upper side of leaves also slightly hairy, the petiole with both scales and hairs. **H:** 7-15 cm. **Hab:** Rock crevices and lava fields. Rather common in some areas. **Sim:** Alpine Woodsia (see 232A). Green Spleenwort (227). The Oblong Woodsia is easily identified by the hairs. **I:** Liðfætla. (Lady-fern family). — **Alpine Woodsia** *Woodsia alpina* resembles Oblong Woodsia, but has shorter, less divided leaflets, and is almost glabrous, except the indusium which tapers into hairs. It is rare; found only in lava fields. — **Wilson's Filmy-fern** *Hymenophyllum wilsonii* is a quite small and delicate fern. The leaves are green, 2-3 mm long, thin, membranous, with dark midrib; the petioles slender as hairs, erect on horizontal rhizome. Only known in one locality in the South. **I:** Mosaburkni. (Filmy-fern family).

Lateral leaflet (m. 1.6)

233 Brittle Bladder-fern
Cystopteris fragilis

Horizontal rhizome with bipinnate leaves. Primary leaflets stand slightly apart from each other, broader at the base, tapering towards the tip. Secondary leaflets pinnately lobed. Sori in two rows on lower side, rather small; indusium attached at their side when young. Stalk of blade (rachis) brittle and slender, usually dark brown, sometimes green. **H:** 10-25 cm, or even more. **Hab:** Rock crevices, lava fissures and caves, usually in shade. Common. **Sim:** Oblong Woodsia (232) has hairy and scaly fronds, thereby differing clearly from Bladder-fern which is glabrous. Dickie's Bladder-fern (see 233A). **I:** Tófugras. (Lady-fern family). — The Brittle Bladder-fern is by far the most common fern in Iceland, and the only one that is widespread throughout the country. — **Dickie's Bladder-fern** *Cystopteris dickieana* is closely related to Brittle Bladder-fern, but usually regarded as a separate species. The spores have a reticulate pattern on its surface, instead of spiny as on the Brittle Bladder-fern. It can hardly be identified by any other characteristic. The spores are small enough to require microscopic examination to ascertain this difference. The Dickie's Bladder-fern has been found in a few localities, but only in N Iceland.

*Lateral leaflet
(m. 1.3)*

234 Parsley Fern
Cryptogamma crispa

Horizontal rhizome. Leaves light green, 3-7 cm long, on long petiole, compound, three-pinnate. Tertiary leaflets pinnately lobed. Fertile leaves equally compound as sterile ones, but lobes are linear, appearing rotund because the leaf margins are recurved from both sides, partly enclosing the sori. **H:** 8-15 cm. **Hab:** Steep, rocky slopes with lasting snow cover. Very rare. **Sim:** None. **I:** Hlíðaburkni. (Parsley Fern family). — This peculiar fern has only been found in two localities, both in the NW of Iceland, rather richly represented in one of them. It could well be expected to be more widely distributed in this area than presently known.

*Lateral leaflet
(m. 2)*

235 Male-fern
Dryopteris filix-mas

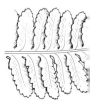

Thick, horizontal rhizome with large, upright, semi-bipinnate fronds, which may reach 1 m in length. Lateral leaflets about 10 cm long and 2-2.5 cm broad in basal part, but tapering towards the point. Secondary leaflets dentate, with 5-10 round sori in two rows underneath. Indusium persistent, slightly reniform to almost round, covering centre of sorus. Stalk represents a quarter or more of frond length, covered in lower part with brown scales. **H:** 30-80 cm. **Hab:** Lava fissures and clefts, grassy slopes or woodland. Rather rare. **Sim:** Lady-fern (236). The Male-fern differs in less incised secondary leaflets, and in the large, reniform indusium. Buckler-fern (see 237). **I:** Stóriburkni. (Lady-fern family).

Lateral leaflet (1:1) and lobe with sori (m. 1.8)

236 Lady-fern
Athyrium filix-femina

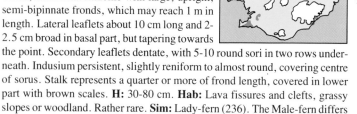

Thick, horizontal rhizome with large, upright, bipinnate or semi-bipinnate fronds. The rachis with scales in the lower part or nearly glabrous. Lateral, primary leaflets about 10 cm long, 1.5-2.5 cm broad from base through centre, tapering towards tip. Secondary leaflets deeply lobed, usually with 8-14 reniform or oblong clusters of sporangia in two rows on lower side. Indusium consists of a membranous flap extending over the cluster from one side. **H:** 30-60 cm. **Hab:** Lava fissures, vegetated slopes and woodland. Scattered to widespread in the lowland of the West and South. **Sim:** Male-fern (233). The Lady-fern differs in more incised secondary leaflets and elongate sporangial clusters with indusium attached on one side. Alpine Lady-fern (see 236A). Buckler-fern (see 237). **I:** Fjöllaufungur. (Lady-fern family). — **Alpine Lady-fern** *Athyrium distentifolium* resembles Lady-fern, but is usually rather smaller. It is distinguished by the round sori, and evanescent indusium. The dissection of the blade is the same, and these two ferns can hardly be distinguished when not fertile. The Alpine Lady-fern always grows in ravines, dells or snowbeds, and only in districts with heavy snow cover.

Lateral leaflet (1:1) and lobe with sori (m. 2)

237 Northern Buckler-fern
Dryopteris assimilis

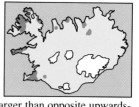

Thick, horizontal rhizome with large, upright, three-pinnate fronds. Primary leaflets obliquely rhomboid or nearly triangular, tapering to a point, broadest near base (4-6 cm); lower, downwards-pointing secondary leaflets much larger than opposite upwards-pointing ones. Tertiary leaflets deeply lobed. Sporangial clusters nearly round, or slightly reniform. Indusium long-lasting. Stalk of frond one third to half of total frond length, lower part usually densely brown-scaled. **H:** 30-80 cm. **Hab:** Lava fissures, between boulders, vegetated hollows and brushwood. Rather rare. **Sim:** Male-fern and Lady-fern (235, 236). The Northern Buckler-fern differs in more compoundly divided frond (at least three-pinnate), with relatively long stalk; also in the unequal size of the secondary leaflets on each side of the lowest primary leaflets. **I:** Dílaburkni. (Lady-fern family).

Lateral leaflet (r. 0.5)

238 Beech Fern
Thelypteris phegopteris

Horizontal rhizome with long-stalked, bipinnate leaves; the stalk two or three times longer than the blade, which is triangular in outline as primary leaflets get gradually longer towards the base. Lowest pair directed slightly downwards. Secondary leaflets usually dentate in lower part, entire in upper part of frond. Sporangial clusters in rows along margin of lower side of leaflets, round, without indusium. **H:** 10-30 cm. **Hab:** Lava fissures, as undergrowth in brushwood, grassy slopes and fertile depressions, occasionally in thermal soil. Widespread in the West. **Sim:** None, easily distinguished from other ferns by the triangular shape of the blade. **I:** Þríhyrnuburkni. (Beech-fern family).

Lateral leaflet (m. 1.2)

239 Oak Fern
Gymnocarpium dryopteris

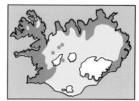

Horizontal rhizome with bi- to three-pinnate frond, appearing trifoliolate as lowest leaflets are almost as large as all other leaflets combined. Leaf stalk very slender, sparsely scaled in lower part. Secondary leaflets pinnate or pinnatifid, with obtuse lobes. Sporangial clusters round, indusium absent. **H:** 10-30 cm. **Hab:** In woodland and dwarf-shrub heaths as undergrowth, also in lava fissures. Widespread. **Sim:** None, differs from other ferns by the trifoliolate appearance of the blade. **I:** Þrílaufungur. (Lady-fern family).

Leaflet with sori (m. 1.5)

240 Common Nettle

Urtica dioeca

Flowers very small, in compound, knotted inflorescences in leaf axils. Perianth leaves four, 1 mm long, greyish green. Four stamens in male flowers, one pistil in female flowers.

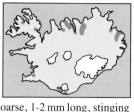

Stems, petioles and inflorescence covered with coarse, 1-2 mm long, stinging hairs on elevated base. Stem quadrangular. Leaves opposite, 5-10 cm long and 1.5-6 cm broad, stalked. Blade sparsely covered with stinging hairs, ovate or cordate, coarsely dentate. **H:** 40-120 cm. **Hab:** Only in populated areas, alien or cultivated. Rare. **Sim:** Small Nettle (see 240A). **Fl:** July. **I:** Brenninetla. (Nettle family). — **Small Nettle** *Urtica urens* is a smaller plant growing along shores or in vegetable gardens. It differs in bisexual flowers, smaller and more roundish, coarsely dentate leaves with more spreading teeth.

Leaf
(r. 0.4)

241 Dwarf Birch

Betula nana

Low shrub with woody branches and brown bark. Flowers unisexual in short spikes called catkins. Female catkins covered with three-lobed scales, three flowers in each catkin.

Female flowers with single, two-styled pistil. Fruit is a narrow-winged nutlet. Male flowers with two divided stamens. Leaves nearly round, 6-8 mm wide, toothed, glabrous, on short petiole. **H:** 20-60 cm. **Hab:** Dwarf-shrub heaths, mires. Common, esp. in the North. **Sim:** Dwarf Willow (see 243). Easily distinguished from Downy Birch (242) by smaller, round leaves. **Fl:** May. **I:** Fjalldrapi. (Birch family).

Leaf
(m. 2.6)

242 Downy Birch

Betula pubescens

Shrub or tree with light greyish-brown or dark reddish-brown bark, easily peeling off. Monoecious with unisexual flowers in catkins. Female catkins erect at flowering time, 2 cm

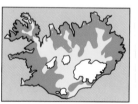

long. Scale leaves three-lobed, three flowers within each scale, each with one two-styled pistil. Fruit is a small, rather broad-winged nutlet. Male catkins with two divided stamens. Leaves dentate, ovate, pinnate-veined, pointed, 2-4.5 cm long, stalked, both leaves and young twigs slightly pubescent. **H:** 1-12 m. **Hab:** Forms scrub or woods in moderately dry soil from the lowland up to 400-450 m. Growth form varies with local climate; dense and low scrub prevails along coast and in stormy and oceanic climate, taller brushwood and trees further inland, esp. in the more continental districts. Common. **Sim:** Dwarf Birch (see 241). **Fl:** May-June. **I:** Birki. (Birch family). — Here and there a hybrid between Downy Birch and Dwarf Birch may be found, more frequently in the N of Iceland, where Dwarf Birch is more common.

Leaf
(r. 0.7)

243 Dwarf Willow
Salix herbacea

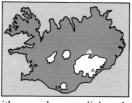

Small shrub with roundish, finely dentate, short-stalked leaves, the youngest leaves sparsely pubescent, becoming glabrous, 0.8-1.5 cm wide. Flowers unisexual in short catkins on separate individuals. Male flowers (right) with one, elongate, light-coloured or reddish bract, two stamens with yellow anthers. Female flowers (left) each with a short bract and single, elongate, bottle-shaped, dark red pistil, terminating in a beak. Fruit a dark red, nearly glabrous capsule. Seeds with long, white hairs. **H:** 5-20 cm. **Hab:** Heathland, snowbeds and depressions in mountains. Common. **Sim:** Dwarf Birch (241). The Dwarf Willow is easily distinguished when in fruit; the leaves are much more finely denticulate than on Dwarf Birch. **Fl:** May-June. **I:** Grasvíðir. (Willow family). — The Dwarf Willow is favoured by grazing sheep, and known by many Icelanders as "smjörlauf" (butter-leaf). The four common willows in Iceland quite frequently form hybrids, which are difficult to identify.

Leaf
(m. 2)

244 Woolly Willow
Salix lanata

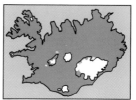

Dioecious shrub with densely haired, elliptic to ovate, pinnate-veined, 3-5 cm long and 1.5-2.5 cm broad leaves. Flowers unisexual in 2.5-8 cm long catkins. Male catkins with long-haired bracts, stamens with bright yellow anthers. Female catkins maturing later, bracts short with long, white tuft of hairs, the pistil or fruit green or yellowish green, glabrous. **H:** 0.5-2 m, usually not reaching full length where grazing is heavy. **Hab:** Heathland, dry slopes and sandy banks. **Sim:** Bluish Willow (245). Woolly Willow can be distinguished by the glabrous fruits, and more densely grey-haired, broader leaves. Flowerless plants can be distinguished by small stipules at the base of the leaves, clearly visible on leafy shoots. These stipules are usually not present on Bluish Willow. **Fl:** May. **I:** Loðvíðir. (Willow family). — The Woolly Willow is a characteristic species for sandy, erosive soils in the Central Highlands and in some parts of the tufaceous districts in Iceland. In some areas, like in Hólsfjöll in the NE, it has for many years been harvested for haymaking. The Icelandic names for Woolly Willow and Bluish Willow are frequently confused, since the Icelandic name "grávíðir" is in many districts generally used for Woolly Willow. Both species often form hybrids, which can be quite variable in character.

Fruit
(m. 6)

245 Bluish Willow
Salix callicarpaea

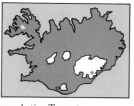

Rather low, dioecious shrub, with elliptic to ovate, 2-4 cm long and 1-1.5 cm broad, hairy leaves, esp. along margin and on lower side. Flowers in 2-6 cm long catkins, unisexual. Catkin scales with long hairs, dark red or blackish towards tip. Two stamens, anthers red. Pistils and fruits densely grey-pubescent. Stigma four-parted, dark red. Seeds with long hair-tuft. **H:** 15-60 cm. **Hab:** Heathland and slopes, esp. in the mountains. Common. **Sim:** Woolly Willow (see 244). Tea-leaved Willow (see 246). **Fl:** May-June. **I:** Grávíðir. (Willow family). — The Icelandic name "grávíðir" is in some districts applied to the Woolly Willow, a frequent cause of misunderstanding when the two species are discussed.

Fruit (m. 6)

246 Tea-leaved Willow
Salix phylicifolia

Large dioecious shrub with lanceolate to elliptic, glabrous leaves (undeveloped leaves slightly hairy), shiny on top, glaucous underneath, 3-5 cm long and 1-2 cm broad. Leaf margin revolute. Branches reddish yellow to reddish brown, glabrous. Flowers in 2-4 cm long catkins, unisexual. Catkin scales long-haired, tawny. Two stamens in each male flower. Pistil hairy, style and stigma yellowish green. **H:** 1-5 m, taller in inland areas than along the coast. Quite low where grazing is heavy. **Hab:** Meadows and river banks, slopes and heathland with moist soil, sometimes forming undergrowth in damp birch woods. Common. **Sim:** Bluish Willow (245) has similar leaves. The leaves of the Tea-leaved Willow are more shiny, and glabrous when mature; their margin is usually very finely denticulate as opposed to completely entire on Bluish Willow. **Fl:** May-June. **I:** Gulvíðir. (Willow family).

Leaf (1:1)

247 Aspen
Populus tremula

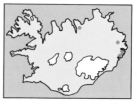

Small tree or shrub, usually creeping; not known to flower in Iceland, but reproduces easily through root stocks. Leaves on long stalk. Blade round or ovate, sometimes slightly pointed, bluntly dentate, usually 2-6 cm wide, green on top, glaucous underneath, nearly glabrous except along veins. Leaf stalk and young branches pubescent. **H:** Up to 6 m, but usually kept low in the wild by grazing. **Hab:** Heaths and woodland. Very rare. **Sim:** None. Easily distinguished from birch and willows by the leaves. **I:** Blæösp. (Willow family).

Scale of catkin (m. 5)

248 Greater Plantain
Plantago major

Flowers small and inconspicuous in dense, 2-12 cm long spike. Corolla brownish with pointed lobes. Sepals four, blunt, green, with membranous margin. Stamens four. Single pistil maturing into a capsule which opens by lateral slit. Leaves in basal rosette, long-petioled. Blade ovate to elliptic, nearly entire, with curved, parallel veins, 2.5-10 cm long and 2-8 cm broad. **H:** 5-30 cm. **Hab:** Frequent in thermal soil near warm springs, usually dwarfish. Alien along paths and roads in populated areas. **Sim:** None. Easily distinguished from Ribwort Plantain (249) by the leaf shape. **Fl:** June-July. **I:** Græðisúra. (Plantain family).

*Leaf
(r. 0.4)*

249 Ribwort Plantain
Plantago lanceolata

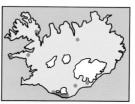

Flowers small, in dense, short, nearly round spike. Corolla brownish, membranous, 4 mm long, split half way down into four pointed lobes. Sepals 2-3 mm long, dark brown-tipped, membranous with green midrib near base. Stamens four with large, 2-3 mm long anthers. Pistil with one, rather long style. Stem hairy, leafless. All leaves basal, long-stalked; blade lanceolate, pointed, parallel-veined, 5-12 cm long and 1-2 cm broad. **H:** 15-35 cm. **Hab:** Grassy slopes and fertile cliffsides. Widespread in the Eyjafjöll and Mýrdalur Districts, otherwise quite rare. **Sim:** None. **Fl:** July. **I:** Selgresi. (Plantain family). — The Ribwort Plantain is a heat-loving plant and grows in southern slopes of those districts with the highest mean temperature in Iceland. In the North it is found only in thermal soil.

*Leaf
(r. 0.4)*

250 Sea Plantain
Plantago maritima

Flowers small and inconspicuous, four-parted, in rather long, dense terminal spike. Corolla tube light greenish, hairy. Petal lobes violet-tinted with broad membranous margin. Sepals green, with membranous margin. Stamens four with yellow anthers. One, single-styled pistil. Fruit is an elongate capsule, 2-3 mm long, opening by lateral slit. Stem with appressed hairs, leafless. All leaves in basal rosette, linear or slightly channelled, thick, 3-5 mm broad, 10-20 cm long, usually short-haired or, rarely, glabrous. **H:** 5-30 cm. **Hab:** Cliffs and slopes, both along the coast and further inland, damp river banks, salt marshes. Common. **Sim:** None. **Fl:** June. **I:** Kattartunga. (Plantain family).

*Leaf
(r. 0.5)*

251 Long-stalked Orache
Atriplex longipes

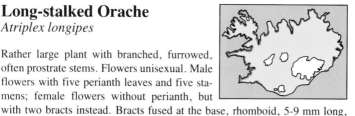

Rather large plant with branched, furrowed, often prostrate stems. Flowers unisexual. Male flowers with five perianth leaves and five stamens; female flowers without perianth, but with two bracts instead. Bracts fused at the base, rhomboid, 5-9 mm long, green or reddish, sometimes stalked. One two-styled pistil. Leaves opposite, stalked, 2-5 cm long and 0.5-2 cm broad, ovate, rhomboid to lanceolate, often reddish-violet; leaves, stem and bracts covered with minute, white, blister-shaped salt hairs, which give the plant a rime-grey surface. **H:** Stems 15-35 cm long, frequently prostrate. **Hab:** Sandy and gravelly beaches. Common, restricted to the seashore. **Sim:** Babington's Orache (see 252). **Fl:** June-July. **I:** Hrímblaðka. (Goosefoot family).

Leaves
(r. 0.7)

252 Babington's Orache
Atriplex glabriuscula

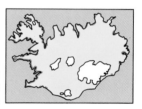

Rather large plant with branched, furrowed, often prostrate stems. Flowers unisexual. Male flowers with five green or reddish perianth leaves and five stamens. Female flowers without perianth, but with two bracts instead; the bracts rhomboid, thick and gristly at the base, fused from below, one third to almost half way up, 6-12 mm long. Single, two-styled pistil. Leaves opposite, stalked, 3-7 cm long and 1-4 cm broad, ovate-lanceolate, broadly rhomboid or nearly triangular; the larger leaves with almost right-angled base, green or violet-tinted. Whole plant covered with minute, blister-like salt-hairs, which give it a rime-grey surface. **H:** Stems 20-40 cm long, often prostrate. **Hab:** Sandy and gravelly beaches. Widespread along the shore. **Sim:** Long-stalked Orache (251). The Babington's Orache usually has broader leaves with a more truncate base, often more green. The bracts are connected further up, appearing inflated or swollen. **Fl:** June-July. **I:** Hélublaðka. (Goosefoot family). — The subdivision of the Orache genus is rather complicated, and specialists have not always agreed which species are present in Iceland or how they should be distinguished. The two orache species described here are closely related, and can produce hybrids. Distinction by the leaves alone is not considered adequate; mature fruits with bracts are required as well. — **Fat-hen** *Chenopodium album* is an unstable alien in Iceland, related to Orache. It has an upright stem, ovate to lanceolate, green leaves, in particular the upper leaves often with rime-grey surface. Occurs in vegetable gardens, waste places and elsewhere in populated areas.

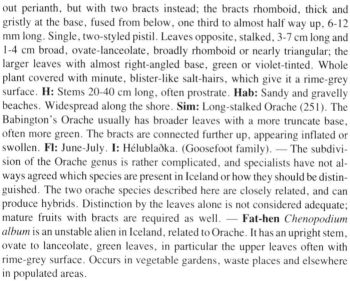

Leaf
(r. 0.5)

253 Common Sorrel
Rumex acetosa

Many flowers in raceme-like inflorescences in leaf axils, unisexual and dioecious. Perianth leaves six; green, red-bordered or entirely red on male flowers, 2-3 mm long, with membranous margin. Stamens six. Female flowers with three recurved perianth leaves and three upright ones appressed to three-sided pistil; three compoundly branched stigmas project out in between perianth leaves. Stem furrowed. Leaves alternate, with sheathing base, arrow-shaped, the lower ones stalked. **H:** 20-40 cm. **Hab:** Grassy plains, fertilized homefields, heathland and fertile slopes. Very common. **Sim:** Sheep's Sorrel (254). The Common Sorrel differs by shape of leaves: the two basal ears point downwards, instead of spreading straight out as on Sheep's Sorrel. **Fl:** May-June. **I:** Túnsúra. (Dock family).

Leaf (r. 0.6)

254 Sheep's Sorrel
Rumex acetosella

Many flowers in raceme-like inflorescences, unisexual, dioecious. Perianth leaves six, usually red, rarely green, 1.5-2 mm long. Three outer perianth leaves narrower than the inner ones; reflexed on mature fruits, while the larger inner ones are appressed to the nutlets. Stamens six with red anthers. Foliage leaves stalked, spear-shaped or lanceolate. Blade 2-6 cm long, 2-20 mm broad with outwards-directed ears near the base. **H:** 10-30 cm. **Hab:** Gravelly, dry soil, also as alien in homefields. Frequently covering large areas where gravelly deserts have been fertilized. Rather common. **Sim:** Common Sorrel (see 253). **Fl:** June. **I:** family).

Leaf (1:1)

255 Northern Dock
Rumex longifolius

Tall plant with round, furrowed, rather thick (5-15 mm) stem and many small flowers in compound inflorescences. Flowers stalked, bisexual; perianth 6-leaved. The three inner perianth leaves appressed to the fruit, becoming large, elliptic to cordate at maturity, dentate. Outer perianth leaves narrower and shorter, green, red-bordered and becoming revolute. Stamens six. Single, three-sided pistil with three red, branched stigmas. Leaves stalked, lanceolate, with strong midrib, undulate or curly margin, and mucous sheath at the base. **H:** 50-130 cm. **Hab:** Introduced, stabilized alien in populated areas, waste places, dumps, roadsides, sometimes forming continuous cover in abandoned homefields. Common. **Sim:** None. **Fl:** June-July. **I:** Njóli. (Dock family). — **Curled Dock** *Rumex crispus* is a rare alien in a few places; it resembles Northern Dock but has a more curled leaf margin, and the inner perianth leaves are entire.

Fruit with perianth (m. 5)

256 Mountain Sorrel
Oxyria digyna

Flowers small and numerous in compound, raceme-like inflorescences on stems. Perianth leaves four, green, nearly round, unequal-sized, 1-2 mm long. Stamens six with yellow or reddish pink anthers. Single, two-styled pistil; stigmas red, compoundly branched. Fruit a two-winged nut, protruding from flower, 3-5 mm long. Leaves thick, reniform, palmate-veined, 2-6 cm wide, long-stalked, glabrous, mainly basal; stem-leaves with basal sheath clasping stem. **H:** 15-40 cm. **Hab:** Ravines, cliffs, gravelly slopes and rocky ground. Common, esp. at higher altitudes. **Sim:** None; easily distinguished from other sorrels by the leaf shape. **Fl:** May-June. **I:** Ólafssúra. (Dock family).

Leaf (1:1)

257 Frog Orchid
Coeloglossum viride

Flowers in single raceme at the top of stem, epigynous. Outer perianth leaves three, ovate, reddish-brown or violet-tinted, 4-6 mm long and 2-3 mm broad; two of the inner perianth leaves pointing upwards, linear, 1 mm broad, blunt-tipped, but one (the lip) pointing downwards, 7-8 mm long, three-lobed, the central lobe shorter than the others. Pistil below perianth, oblong, distorted. Fruit with numerous, extremely small seeds. Stem glabrous with a few, parallel-veined leaves; the upper ones narrowly lanceolate, the lower ones broader, 1.5-2 cm, elliptic to obovate, with silvery sheen on lower side. **H:** 12-25 cm. **Hab:** Fertile depressions in slopes, heathland and brushwood, more common towards the mountains than in the lowland. **Sim:** Northern Green Orchid (194), Small-white Orchid (195). The Frog Orchid differs in the shape of the lip, and the reddish brown flowers. **Fl:** June-July. **I:** Barnarót. (Orchid family).

Flower (m. 3)

258 Coralroot Orchid
Corallorhiza trifida

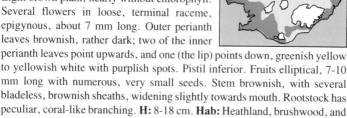

Light brown plant, nearly without chlorophyll. Several flowers in loose, terminal raceme, epigynous, about 7 mm long. Outer perianth leaves brownish, rather dark; two of the inner perianth leaves point upwards, and one (the lip) points down, greenish yellow to yellowish white with purplish spots. Pistil inferior. Fruits elliptical, 7-10 mm long with numerous, very small seeds. Stem brownish, with several bladeless, brownish sheaths, widening slightly towards mouth. Rootstock has peculiar, coral-like branching. **H:** 8-18 cm. **Hab:** Heathland, brushwood, and poor-soiled pastures and meadows. Widespread, never in quantities. **Sim:** None. **Fl:** June-July. **I:** Kræklurót. (Orchid family).

Flower (m. 2)

220

259 Lesser Twayblade
■□
□
Listera cordata

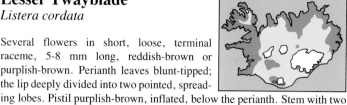

Several flowers in short, loose, terminal raceme, 5-8 mm long, reddish-brown or purplish-brown. Perianth leaves blunt-tipped; the lip deeply divided into two pointed, spreading lobes. Pistil purplish-brown, inflated, below the perianth. Stem with two opposite, sessile, 1-2 cm long, cordate to broadly ovate leaves; one brownish, bladeless sheath at the base. **H:** 8-15 cm. **Hab:** Among dwarfshrubs in heathland, ravine-slopes and hollows. Fairly widespread. **Sim:** None. Easily distinguished from Common Twayblade by leaf shape and size. **Fl:** July. **I:** Hjartatvíblaðka. (Orchid family). — Lesser Twayblade is a very inconspicuous plant when it occurs as undergrowth underneath dwarfshrubs. The colours are easily hidden by the surroundings, and the plant is therefore easily overlooked by those who are not familiar with it.

Flower (m. 6)

260 Common Twayblade
□■
□
Listera ovata

Tall plant, the flowers in a 5-8 cm long terminal raceme. Flowers with five erect, greenish, 3-4 mm long perianth leaves, and one 6-10 mm long, light tawny or greenish lip, divided into two rather long and spreading lobes. Pistil appears like a short, inflated knob below the perianth. Two ovate to elliptic, entire, parallel-veined leaves on lower part of stem, 6-12 cm long and 2.5-6 cm broad. **H:** 30-60 cm. **Hab:** Woodland and grassy hollows. Rare. **Sim:** Easily distinguished by the two large ovate leaves. Lesser Twayblade (259) has much smaller, cordate leaves. **Fl:** June-July. **I:** Eggtvíblaðka. (Orchid family).

Flower (m. 3)

261 Small Adder's-tongue
□□
■
Ophioglossum azoricum

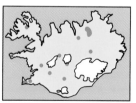

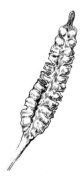

One to three leaves grow from short, erect rootstock. Leaves deeply cleft into sterile lobe and fertile lobe. Sterile blade lanceolate to elliptic, entire, net-veined, 2-4 cm long and 5-15 mm broad. Fertile lobe with single, one-sided sporangial spike, about 10-15 mm long. Sporangia closely packed in two rows lengthwise on spike. **H:** 3-10 cm. **Hab:** Restricted to thermal soil, in clay flats, grassy soil or along springs or warm stream banks. Very rare. **Sim:** None. **I:** Naðurtunga. (Adder's-tongue family).

Sporangial spike (m. 3)

262 Highland Cudweed
Omalotheca norvegica

Many flowers in small (5 mm) heads forming raceme-like inflorescence on top of stem. Heads surrounded by bracts which are green in centre with broad, usually blackish brown membranous margin, entire, shiny, ovate to long-elliptic, with blunt tip. Tube of corolla hair-like, 3-4 mm long, 0.1-0.2 mm wide, light-coloured, reddish towards tip and terminating in five petal lobes, some of the tubes expanding into a 0.5-1 mm broad bell at the top. Corolla surrounded by white pappus. Leaves lanceolate, 5-10 cm long, broadest (8-18 mm) near tip, tapering to a stalk, densely tomentose, esp. on lower side. **H:** 15-30 cm. **Hab:** Hollows and below hillsides in mountainous areas, esp. those with heavy snow layers. Fairly widespread, rare in the South. **Sim:** Heath Cudweed (263). The Highland Cudweed differs through the long, broad leaves and shorter inflorescence. **Fl:** July. **I:** Fjandafæla. (Daisy family).

Leaf
(r. 0.6)

263 Heath Cudweed
Omalotheca sylvatica

Flowers many in small (5 mm) heads which are arranged into long terminal raceme. Bracts green in the centre, with a broad membranous margin, 3-4 mm long, 1-2 mm broad, ovate to long-elliptic, entire, shiny. Tube of corolla slender as a hair, 0.1-0.2 mm, light green underneath, the tip brownish, sometimes broadening to 0.5 mm at the mouth; petal lobes five. Stem leafy. Leaves 3-8 cm long and 2-5 mm broad, densely grey-tomentose, esp. the lower side, entire or slightly dentate. **H:** 10-25 cm. **Hab:** Steep, dry southern slopes. Rather rare. **Sim:** Highland Cudweed (see 262). **Fl:** July. **I:** Grájurt. (Daisy family).

Leaf
(m. 1.4)

264 Dwarf Cudweed
Omalotheca supina

Several flowers in few, small heads at the top of stem. Heads surrounded by blackish brown involucral bracts; bracts green around the midrib, sometimes with a purple zone. Flowers all tubular, the tube 3-4 mm long, with five lobes, brown at the tip with purple zone and light green at the bottom; only the brown tip visible from the outside. Whorl of hairs around the fruit. Stem and leaves tomentose; leaves nearly linear, tapering towards the tip, 1.5-3 mm broad and 1-1.5 cm long. **H:** 2-8 cm. **Hab:** Snowbeds and slopes in mountains; restricted in the lowland to districts with heavy snow cover in winter and spring. Common. **Sim:** Alpine Cat's-foot (see 266). Marsh Cudweed (see 265). **Fl:** June. **I:** Grámulla. (Daisy family).

Leaf
(m. 3)

265 Marsh Cudweed
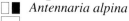
Filaginella uliginosa

Annual plant with several flowers in small, densely clustered heads with pointed involucral bracts, membranous and brownish above, green with purple zone below. Corolla tube 1-1.5 mm long, very slender (0.1-0.2 mm), yellowish green. Sepals transformed into a whorl of hairs (pappus). Stem repeatedly branched, densely white-tomentose. Leaves opposite, lanceolate to linear, densely tomentose, 10-25 mm long, 2-4 mm broad, broadest in front. **H:** 5-12 cm. **Hab:** Clay flats or mossy ground in thermal areas. Rare. **Sim:** Dwarf Cudweed (264). The Marsh Cudweed differs in the repeatedly branched stem, and in lacking basal leaf rosettes. **Fl:** July-August. **I:** Grámygla. (Daisy family).

Leaf (m. 2)

266 Alpine Cat's-foot
Antennaria alpina

Dioecious plant, many flowers in several small (5 mm) terminal heads, which resemble tufts of grey hairs. Involucral bracts 3-5 mm long, green at the base, blackish brown in the upper part, lanceolate. Corolla of male flowers yellow, purple on female flowers, slender like a hair (0.1 mm), 3-4 mm long, surrounded by whorl of numerous white hairs (pappus). Style protrudes from tube of female flowers; stigma divided. Stem tomentose, leafy; basal leaves in rosette, broadest near front (2-3 mm) with short terminal point. **H:** 5-12 cm. **Hab:** Gravelly soil and dry slopes in the lowland, or in rocky soil in the mountains. Rare. **Sim:** Dwarf Cudweed (262). The Alpine Cat's-foot differs by the shape of the basal leaves; it never grows in snowbeds like the Dwarf Cudweeed. **Fl:** June. **I:** Fjallalójurt. (Daisy family).

Leaf (m. 4)

267 Juniper
Juniperus communis

Dioecious shrub with needle-shaped leaves; needles 8-12 mm long, 1-2 mm broad, sharp-pointed, channelled on top and keeled underneath. Many male flowers in very small (2-3 mm) cones in leaf axils. Cone leaves tawny, triangular to rhomboid. Female flowers also formed in small cones; only the three uppermost cone scales are fertile growing large and fusing into a berry-like fruit about 8 mm wide; the berries first green, then blue. Lower female cone leaves form small appendix attached to base of berry. **H:** 30-120 cm, usually prostrate but sometimes a more or less erect shrub. **Hab:** Heathland, lava fields, brushwood and hill edges. Common. **Sim:** None. **I:** Einir. (Cypress family).

Fruit (m. 2.8)

226

268 Crowberry

Empetrum nigrum

Flowers minute, inconspicuous, three-parted, surrounded by a few, roundish, red bracts. Petals dark red, 2-2.5 mm long, spatulate, recurved; the sepals brownish, involute, nearly round. Stamens three, 5-7 mm long, dark purple, protruding far out of flower. Single pistil matures to a berry-like drupe with 6-9 small stones. Fruit first green, then red and finally black, 5-8 mm wide. Shoots woody, leafless below, dense-leaved above. Leaves oblong, blunt, 4-6 mm long and 1.5 mm broad, thick and hollow inside. Leaf margins are in reality recurved to form a tube with a white strip where the margins meet. **H:** procumbent shrub, the shoots commonly 5-12 cm tall. **Hab:** Wide variety of habitats: heathland, gravel hills, moss mats, lava fields and even bogs. Very common. **Sim:** Blue Heath (see 34). **Fl:** April-May. **I:** Krækilyng. (Crowberry family). — Crowberry is the most common wild berry in Iceland, and is harvested every year for human consumption. It has been divided into two subspecies: ssp. *nigrum*, which has unisexual flowers and is only found in lowland areas, and ssp. *hermaphroditum*, which has bisexual flowers and coarser leaves. The latter is the most common type here, in the lowland as well as in the mountains. It has larger berries, and the stamens remain attached when they are harvested.

Flower (m. 5)

269 Fir Clubmoss

Huperzia selago

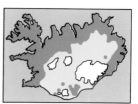

Several dense-leaved, procumbent or upright, finger-like stems, branching mainly at the base, but sometimes also higher up. Leaves 6-8 mm long, 1-1.5 mm broad, entire, needle-shaped, acute. Fertile leaves of same shape as sterile leaves, scattered in the upper part. Small sprouts are formed here and there in leaf axils, with broader, blunt leaves. **H:** 5-12 cm. **Hab:** Heathland, depressions and between boulders in the mountains, sometimes in lava-fissures and moss mats in the lowland. Rather common. **Sim:** Interrupted Clubmoss (271). The Fir Clubmoss differs by the sporangia scattered throughout the stem, by the sprouts, and by never forming elongated runners like the Interrupted Clubmoss. **I:** Skollafingur. (Clubmoss family).

Sporophyll with sporangium (m. 7)

270 Alpine Clubmoss

Diphazium alpinum

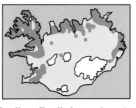

Long, prostrate stems with ascending branches. Leaves 3-4 mm long, involute, usually with blunt tip, appressed, the shoots therefore appearing narrower than on other clubmosses. Sporangia in the axils of fertile leaves in terminal spikes. Fertile leaves broad-based, pointed, with irregularly dentate margin, each bearing one sporangium. **H:** Upright branches 8-15 cm, prostrate stems 50 cm or more. **Hab:** Depressions and snowbeds, also in dwarf-shrub heaths, but only in districts with prolonged snow cover. Rather common. **Sim:** None. **I:** Litunarjafni. (Clubmoss family).

Sporophyll with sporangium (m. 12)

271 Interrupted Clubmoss

Lycopodium annotinum.

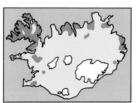

Long, prostrate stems with ascending, dense-leaved side branches, some of which bear a 1-2 cm long sporangial cone. Leaves almost entire, needle-shaped, pointed, shiny, 4-7 mm long and 1 mm broad, light green. Sporangial leaves densely crowded in terminal cone, light green or tawny, broader than the sterile leaves, nearly round, with whitish, incised margin. **H:** Upright branches 5-15 cm, the prostrate stems often more than 50 cm. **Hab:** Brushwood, dwarf-shrub heath and slopes. Rather rare. **Sim:** Alpine Clubmoss (see 269). **I:** Lyngjafni. (Clubmoss family. — Stag's-horn Clubmoss *Lycopodium clavatum* is extremely rare in Iceland, found only in one locality. It resembles Interrupted Clubmoss, but differs by small tuft of hairs on the leaf point, and by two sporangial cones terminally on slender, upright branches.

Sporophyll with sporangium (m. 10)

272 Lesser Clubmoss

Selaginella selaginoides

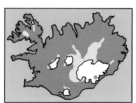

Small plant with repeatedly branched, delicate, dense-leaved, dark green, ascending stems. Leaves 2-3 mm long, 1 mm broad, tapering to a sharp point, with denticulate margin. Fertile stems longer than sterile ones, erect, with appressed leaves below, more outstanding sporophylls in upper part, with sporangia in the axils. Lower sporangia with four macrospores, 0.5 mm wide, the upper with numerous, yellowish microspores. **H:** 3-8 cm. **Hab:** Dry heathland and pastures. Very common. **Sim:** None; resembles mosses, but differs by the sporangia in the leaf axils. **I:** Mosajafni. (Spikemoss family).

Sporophyll with sporangium (m. 8)

273 Wood Millet
☑☐
☐☐
Milium effusum

Very tall grass with 8-16 mm broad leaves.
Panicle 25-35 cm long, loose, oblong-conical.
Spikelets rotund, awnless, single-flowered,
green or yellowish green. Glumes roundish,
green, 2.5-3.5 mm long, three-nerved. Lemma shorter, shiny. Ligule 3-5 mm
long, pointed or worn. **H:** 1-1.8 m. **Hab:** Sheltered places in slopes and lava
fields, brushwood, between boulders. Rather rare. **Sim:** None. Differs from
all other grasses by the large panicle and broad leaves. **Fl:** July. **I:** Skrautpunt-
ur. (Grass family).

*Spikelet
(m. 6)*

274 Tufted Hair-grass
☐■
☐☐
Deschampsia caespitosa

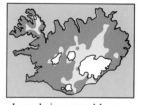

Tall, tufted grass with 2-4 mm broad, very
rough and sharply furrowed leaves. Panicle 15-
20 cm long, conical. Spikelets two-flowered,
violet to dark brown. Lower glume single-
nerved, 3 mm; the upper three-nerved, 3.5 mm. Long hairs around lemma,
which has a dorsal awn at the base. Ligules of upper leaves 5-6 mm long. **H:**
40-120 cm. **Hab:** Fertile grassland, homefields and heathland. Common.
Sim: Common Bent (277). Tufted Hair-grass differs by the rough-ribbed
leaves, appearing white-striped against light, and coarser panicle. **Fl:** June-
July. **I:** Snarrótarpuntur. (Grass family).

*Spikelet
(m. 6.3)*

275 Alpine Hair-grass
☐☐
■☐
Deschampsia alpina

Panicle viviparous, 10-20 cm long. Spikelets
two-flowered, the upper with leaves. Glumes
4-7 mm long, membranous. Lower glume
single-nerved, the upper three-nerved. Lemma
with dorsal awn; long hairs around base. Leaves 2-4 mm broad, very rough,
sharp-ribbed. Ligule 5-6 mm long. **H:** 20-60 cm. **Hab:** Damp and rocky flats,
moist rock ledges or grassland. Common. **Sim:** Differs from other grasses by
large viviparous panicle; leaves like on tuffed Hair-grass (274). **Fl:** June-July.
I: Fjallapuntur. (Grass family).

*Spikelet
(m. 1.5)*

276 Wavy Hair-grass
☐☐
☐■
Deschampsia flexuosa

Average-sized grass with reddish, 10-15 cm
long panicle. Branchlets reddish-violet, wavy.
Spikelets two-flowered. Glumes single-
nerved, membranous, 5-6 mm long. Lemma
with long, sharply bent awn, and white hairs at the base. Basal leaves filiform,
bright green. **H:** 20-70 cm. **Hab:** Dwarf-shrub heath, brushwood and slopes.
Common. **Sim:** Easily distinguished by the panicle; the leaves resemble Arctic Fescue (292), but brighter green and not channelled. **Fl:** July. **I:**
Bugðupuntur. (Grass family).

*Spikelet
(m. 3)*

277 Common Bent
Agrostis capillaris

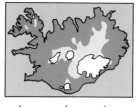

Panicle delicate, reddish-brown, rather large, 8-16 cm long. Spikelets single-flowered. Glumes reddish-brown to purplish, 3-3.5 mm long, one- to three-nerved, rounded or with rough keel. Lemma much shorter, white, twice as long as palea, awnless or with short dorsal awn. Leaves flat, 2-4 mm broad, rough. Ligule very short, truncate, 0.5-1 mm long, the upper ones sometimes longer. **H:** 30-80 cm. **Hab:** Grassy depressions and slopes, woodland and homefields. Common. **Sim:** Other bents (278-279). Common Bent has larger panicle, but the best characteristic is the very short ligule. **Fl:** July. **I:** Hálíngresi. (Grass family).

Spikelet (m. 8)

278 Velvet Bent
Agrostis vinealis

Small grass. Panicle delicate, reddish-brown, rather small. Spikelets single-flowered. Glumes reddish-brown to purplish, 2.5-3 mm long, single-nerved, rounded or with rough keel, pointed. Lemma shorter, with dorsal awn twice as long and exeeding the spikelet. Leaves 1-3 mm broad, ligule 1.5-2.5 mm. **H:** 10-40 cm. **Hab:** Dry slopes, gravel hills and heathland. Common. **Sim:** Other bents (277, 279). Best distinguished by the slender awn sticking out of the spikelets. The ligule is distinctly longer than on Common Bent. **Fl:** July. **I:** Týtulíngresi. (Grass family).

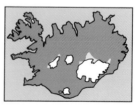

Spikelet (m. 8)

279 Creeping Bent
Agrostis stolonifera

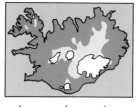

Prostrate grass, often with long runners. Panicle delicate, reddish-brown, 3-10 cm long, rather dense with short, upright branchlets. Spikelet single-flowered. Glumes reddish-brown or purplish, 3-3.5 mm long, single-nerved, pointed, rounded; the nerve often with upwards-directed bristles on dorsal side. Lemma white, twice as long as the palea, with short dorsal awn above centre. Leaves 1.5-4 mm broad, ligule 2-3 mm long. **H:** 15-40 cm. **Hab:** Damp soil, stream- and lake banks, periodically flooded marshland, also dry grassland. Common. **Sim:** Other bents (277-278). The Creeping Bent differs through the runners, which are most pronounced in wet habitats, and denser panicle. Spikelets without long awn, ligule shorter than on Common Bent. **Fl:** July. **I:** Skriðlíngresi. (Grass family).

Spikelet (m. 11)

234

280 Narrow Small-reed
Calamagrostis stricta

Panicle rather delicate, dense, with short branches, pinkish brown, greenish or with violet tint, 3-18 cm long. Spikelets single-flowered. Glumes 3-4 mm long, pointed. White hairs at base of florets, lemma with dorsal awn, which is shorter than the lemma, palea also shorter. Ligule up to 2 mm long on upper sheaths, very short or absent on lower ones. Culm-leaves flat, 2-4 mm broad; shoot-leaves slender, 1-2 mm. **H:** 30-60 cm. **Hab:** Different kinds of moist habitats, mires, bogs, sandy banks of streams and lakes. Common. **Sim:** Creeping Bent (279). The Narrow Small-reed has lighter panicle, longer and narrower shoot-leaves. **Fl:** June-July. **I:** Hálmgresi. (Grass family).

Spikelet
(m. 10)

281 Common Saltmarsh-grass
Puccinellia maritima

Average-sized or rather small, tufted grass. Panicle slender, branchlets upright, the lowest one sometimes directed downwards. Spikelets with variable number of florets, usually 3-8. Glumes short, green to purplish, margin membranous, tip toothed or incised. Upper glume usually twice as long as lower one. Lemma more often green than purplish, 3-4 mm long. Shoot leaves narrow (1-1.5 mm), round and grooved. Culm leaves usually flat or keeled. **H:** 10-30 cm. **Hab:** Saltmarshes, sandy and rocky shores. Common. **Sim:** Reflexed Saltmarsh-grass (see 281A). **Fl:** July. **I:** Sjávarfitjungur. — **Reflexed Saltmarsh-grass** *Puccinellia distans* resembles Common Saltmarsh-grass, grows in dense tufts, usually with longer branchlets in the panicle, partly pointing straight out or downwards. It is not as restricted to the shore, sometimes found near farms further inland, but usually on sandy or gravelly beaches.

Spikelet
(m. 6)

282 Whorl-grass
Catabrosa aquatica

Creeping grass with ascending culms. Panicle conical, 4-7 cm long, with spreading to reflexed branches. Spikelets usually single-flowered. Glumes obtuse, short (1-1.5 mm), green or violet, often with irregularly incised margin. Lemma with three raised nerves, 2.5-3 mm long. Leaves rather short, 2-4 mm broad. Ligule 2-3.5 mm, pointed. **H:** 10-30 cm, creeping runners often longer. **Hab:** Shallow ponds, flooded, sandy flats and ditches. Good spring water indicator in bogs and mires. **Sim:** The panicle is rather characteristic; the runners recall Creeping Bent, but have shorter and broader leaves. **Fl:** June. **I:** Vatnsnarfagras. (Grass family).

Spikelet
(m. 8)

283 Floating Sweet-grass
Glyceria fluitans

■
□□

Large grass with long, slender, rather lax panicle. Spikelets 10-25 mm long, 8-12 flowered.
Glumes short (2-4 mm), membranous, greenish or transparent. Lemma 5-7 nerved, green,
5-7 mm long, with blunt or worn point, short-haired, margin membranous in
upper part. Culms 4-6 mm thick. Leaves 4-10 mm broad. Ligule 6-10 mm
long. **H:** 50-100 cm. **Hab:** Drainage ditches and other water-beds, small
lakes. Only in the South. **Sim:** None. **Fl:** July-August. **I:** Flóðapuntur. (Grass
family).

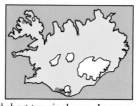

*Spikelet
(m. 1.5)*

284 Yorkshire-fog
Holcus lanatus

□
■□

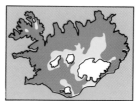

Panicle usually pinkish-violet, 6-15 cm long,
dense. Spikelets two-flowered; the lower floret
bisexual, the upper one unisexual male.
Glumes 4-5 mm long, hairy; the lower glume
with one, the upper with three raised nerves and short terminal awn. Lemma
shiny, green, glabrous with long hairs at the base. Lemma of upper floret with
curved, twisted awn. Culm, leaves and sheaths densely short-haired. Leaves
4-8 mm broad. Ligule short, 1-1.5 mm, hairy. **H:** 30-60 cm. **Hab:** Grassland,
slopes, heathland and ditch-banks. Rare. **Sim:** None; only Spiked Oatgrass
(297) is as distinctly hairy as Yorkshire-fog. **Fl:** June-July. **I:** Loðgresi.
(Grass family).

*Spikelet
(m. 5.5)*

285 Holy-grass
Hierochloë odorata

□
□■

Panicle spreading, 5-12 cm long, light brown.
Spikelets short and broad, three-flowered.
Glumes 5-6.5 mm long, membranous, light
brown, with many rather indistinct veins.
Lemma light brown-haired, sharply pointed. Shoot leaves rather long, 4-6
mm broad, shiny on top, slightly hairy, yellowish green. Culm leaves short.
H: 25-50 cm. **Hab:** Grassy heathland, fertile slopes, brushwood. Widespread. **Sim:** Smooth Meadow-grass (286). The Holy-grass differs through
broader, shiny leaves with sweet taste. Leaf apex not boat-shaped. Sweet Ver-
nal-grass (296) has similar, but shorter and narrower leaves, and the same
sweet taste. It differs from Holy-grass in having small hairs around the ligule.
Fl: July. **I:** Reyrgresi. (Grass family).

*Spikelet
(m. 5)*

286 Smooth Meadow-grass
Poa pratensis

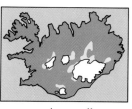

Variable species; panicle 5-15 cm long. Spikelets three- to five-flowered. Glumes usually violet, sharply keeled, pointed, three-nerved. Lemma with woolen hairs at base and on lower part of nerves, pointed, with membranous margin, usually green below, upper part violet. Creeping stolons with leafy shoots, stolons flattened, the leaves folded along keel; the apex shaped like a prow. Ligule absent at lowest stem-leaf sheath, short (1-2 mm) on the upper sheaths. **H:** 20-70 cm. **Hab:** Grassy plains, homefields, fertilized areas; moist soil and mires at higher altitudes. Very common. **Sim:** Rough Meadow-grass (see 286A). Annual Meadow-grass (see 290). Alpine Meadow-grass (287); the Smooth Meadow-grass differs through the creeping stolons with keeled or folded, long shoot-leaves. **Fl:** June-July. **I:** Vallarsveifgras (Grass family). — **Rough Meadow-grass** *Poa trivialis* resembles large Smooth Meadow-grass, but usually has a larger panicle, and smaller, green spikelets. The best characteristic is the very long (4-8 mm), pointed ligule. Prefers wet habitats or seepage water, but also found in seeded grasslands.

Spikelet (m. 5.5)

287 Alpine Meadow-grass
Poa alpina

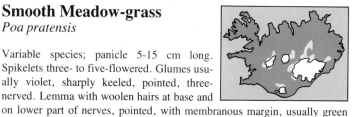

Panicle conical, often viviparous, 2-8 cm long, purplish or red. Spikelets 2-5-flowered; glumes 3-4 mm, sharply keeled, usually violet, three-nerved. Lemma green below, violet above, with membranous margin. Culm leaves rather short and broad, the apex prow-shaped. Ligule about 2 mm. No creeping stolons; leaf shoots generally intravaginal at the base. **H:** 8-35 cm. **Hab:** Gravel hills, heathland, cliffs. Common, esp. in mountains. **Sim:** When not viviparous, the Alpine Meadow-grass may resemble Smooth Meadow-grass (286), but differs through broader culm-leaves, and absence of stolons. **Fl:** June-July. **I:** Fjallasveifgras. (Grass family).

Spikelet (m. 5)

288 Wavy Meadow-grass
Poa flexuosa

Panicle small, dark-violet, slightly drooping. Panicle branchlets slender, upright. Spikelets usually two- or three-flowered. Glumes dark, broad, pointed, 3-4 mm long, three-nerved. Lemma with indistinct nerves, hairy below, with membranous margin and violet zone in upper part. Leaves narrow, 1-2 mm, the uppermost culm leaves close to panicle. Ligule 2-3 mm long, pointed. **H:** 10-20 cm. **Hab:** Gravelly hills and screes. Common at high altitudes. **Sim:** Glaucous Meadow-grass (289). The Wavy Meadow-grass has green, softer and weaker culms, panicle slightly nodding. **Fl:** July-August. **I:** Lotsveifgras. (Grass family).

Spikelet (m. 6)

289 Glaucous Meadow-grass
Poa glauca

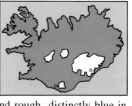

Panicle bluish, rather narrow, 4-8 cm long. Spikelets three- to five-flowered. Glumes 3-4 mm long, dark violet, sharply keeled, pointed, three-nerved. Lemma hairy below and on the nerves. Culms in tufts, usually inclined, stiff and rough, distinctly blue in upper part, leafy in lower half. Ligule short, 1 mm. Leaves rather narrow, 1.5-3 mm. **H:** 15-35 cm. **Hab:** Gravel, rock outcrops and cliffs. Common. **Sim:** Wavy Meadow-grass (see 288). Glaucous Meadow-grass growing in shade is often similar to Wood Meadow-grass (289A). **Fl:** June-July. **I:** Blásveifgras. (Grass family). — **Wood Meadow-grass** *Poa nemoralis* is more green, with longer, more slender culms than Glaucous Meadow-grass, the culm has more numerous leaves (4-5), the panicle less branched with fewer spikelets. Found in woodland and lava fissures. This species can not always be clearly separated from Glaucous Meadow-grass.

Spikelet (m. 5)

290 Annual Meadow-grass
Poa annua

Annual grass, panicle conical, light green, rarely violet-tinted, 2-5 cm long. Spikelets 4-6-flowered. Glumes 1.5-3 mm long, the lower shorter than the upper. Lemma usually 5-nerved; woolen hairs around base or on nerves. Leaves light green, often with some transversal wrinkles. Ligule 1.5-2 mm. Often forming low, dense cover. This grass is difficult to dry and makes poor hay. **H:** 8-35 cm. **Hab:** Paths and tracks, terraces, spoiled plots of cultivated grassland, moderately moist open areas. Common. **Sim:** Smooth Meadow-grass (286). The Annual Meadow-grass has lighter, more yellowish green leaves and panicle; a good characteristic is also the different length of the glumes. **Fl:** June-Oct. **I:** Varpasveifgras. (Grass family).

Spikelet (m. 5)

291 Cock's-foot
Dactylis glomerata

Robust, tall grass, many spikelets densely clustered at the end of branches. Panicle branchlets very rough. Spikelets 3-4-flowered, sparsely to densely haired; glumes violet-tinted or grey, three-nerved, with terminal awn; the central nerve with upwards-directed, sharp points (rough). Lemma greyish, often flushed with violet, terminating in awn, 5-nerved, the central nerve sharply keeled. Anthers light brown to purplish, 3-4 mm long. Leaves broad, 4-7 mm. **H:** 50-120 cm. **Hab:** Seeded pastures and homefields, alien in grassy slopes and along roadsides. Fairly widespread in cultivation. **Sim:** None; easily distinguished by the large, compact clusters of spikelets. **Fl:** August. **I:** Axhnoðapuntur. (Grass family).

Spikelet (m. 4)

292 Arctic Fescue
Festuca richardsonii

Narrow panicle, 3-8 cm long, usually grey to greyish green. Spikelets large, 8-12 mm long, 5-8 flowered, hairy. Glumes 3-6 mm long, pointed. Lemma hairy, five-nerved, sharp-pointed. Creeping runners with long, slender (0.5-1 mm), channelled, often bluish green leaves. **H:** 20-60 cm. **Hab:** Sandy deserts, gravelly soil, cultivated homefields, heathland, breeding places of birds, damp meadows. Very common. **Sim:** Characterized by many-flowered spikelets, hairy, pointed glumes. The leaves resemble those of Viviparous Fescue (293) and Wavy Hairgrass (276), differing from the former by the runners, and from the latter by the more bluish green, channelled leaves. **Fl:** June-July. **I:** Túnvingull. (Grass family). — **Red Fescue** *Festuca rubra* is related to Arctic Fescue and they are often regarded as the same species. Red Fescue is introduced and widespread. It has been grown for many years in cultivated homefields, seeded along recently constructed roads, and for restoration of eroded land. It has longer, reddish culms, larger and slightly nodding panicle compared to the native fescue, also less hairy to glabrous spikelets. — **Meadow Fescue** *Festuca pratensis* is a very rare alien, occasionally cultivated in homefields, possibly native in Mýrdalur. The panicle is long, slightly nodding with 10-18 mm long, 8-13 flowered spikelets. Glumes very short, glabrous; lemma greyish-green, with membranous margin, and worn tip. Leaves flat, 3-6 mm broad.

Spikelet (m. 4)

293 Viviparous Fescue
Festuca vivipara

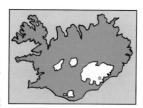

Panicle short, 2-5 cm, always viviparous. Spikelets hairy or glabrous, usually brownish-violet or reddish-purple. Leaves in dense tufts, rather short, narrow, channelled; no creeping runners. **H:** 10-40 cm. **Hab:** Gravelly hills, hill tops, heathland and open soil. Very common. **Sim:** Resembles Arctic Fescue (292) when not in flower, but easily distinguished by the viviparous panicle. **Fl:** June-July. **I:** Blávingull. (Grass family).

Viviparous spikelet (m. 2)

294 Snow Goosegrass
Phippsia algida

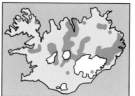

Very low grass, forming small tufts. Culms decumbent, ascending or upright. Panicle slender, resembling spike. Spikelets usually single-flowered. Glumes very short (0.2-0.5 mm), sometimes only one present. Lemma longer (1-1.5 mm) and broader, green to purplish with light brown membranous margin, tip blunt, jagged or pointed. Leaves 1-2 mm broad, with prow-shaped apex; ligule 1 mm. **H:** 2-8 cm. **Hab:** Open soil, wet gravelly soil or flushes from melting snow. Colonizer of revegetating river beds. Rather rare, only at high altitudes or in Central Highlands. **Sim:** Recalls small Whorl-grass (282), but lacks rooting runners, the lemma nerveless. **Fl:** July. **I:** Snænarfagras. (Grass family).

Spikelet (m. 1.7)

295 Hungarian Brome

Bromus inermis

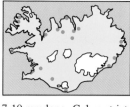

Large grass. Panicle rather large, 10-18 cm long. Spikelets 5-9 flowered, often 2-2.5 cm long. Glumes 5-8 mm long, blunt, rounded, the lower single-nerved and shorter, the upper three-nerved. Lemma with three raised nerves, 7-10 mm long. Culms strict. Numerous, densely leafy, upright shoots. Leaves large, 6-12 mm broad. **H:** 60-120 cm. **Hab:** Used for land reclamation; alien in villages, farms and roadsides. Rather rare. **Sim:** Easily identified by the tall leafy shoots. **Fl:** August. **I:** Sandfax. (Grass family).

Spikelet (m. 1.3)

296 Sweet Vernal-grass

Anthoxanthum odoratum

Many spikelets in slender, 2-4 cm long, spike-like panicle. Spikelets sharp-pointed, the upper twice as long as the lower. Stamens only two. Stigma bifid. Lemma with long, protruding dorsal awn. Leaves flat, 3-5 cm broad. Culm short, round, striate; leaf base often purplish around the sheath; hairs around the ligule. **H:** 20-30 cm. **Hab:** Dry grassy slopes, pastures and heathland. Common. **Sim:** None, see Holy-grass (285). **Fl:** May-June. **I:** Ilmreyr. (Grass family).

Spikelet (m. 3)

297 Spiked Oatgrass

Trisetum spicatum

Panicle slender, spike-like, 2-4 cm long, violet or greyish green. Spikelets two-flowered. Glumes 3.5-4.5 mm long, green below, violet above with membranous margin, pointed; lemma with long, protruding dorsal awn above centre. Culms and sheaths densely pubescent. **H:** 10-30 cm. **Hab:** Heaths, gravel, rock outcrops. Common. **Sim:** Easily distinguished by hairy culms. **Fl:** June-July. Ssp. *pilosiglume* has a larger, more green panicle, occurs mainly in the lowland, but ssp. *spicatum* occurs at high altitudes as well. **I:** Lógresi. (Grass family).

Spikelet (m. 3.5)

298 Blue Moor-grass

Sesleria albicans

Flowers in short (1.5-2 cm), longly ovate, dense, spike-like panicle. Spikelets two-flowered. Glumes 4-5 mm long, membranous, transparent with dark, sharp-pointed midrib. Lemma broad, 5-7 nerved, bluish violet above, the midrib forming short, blue bristle out of the spikelet. Leaf shoots with rather long, 2-4 mm broad leaves, folded along the keel. Ligule very short. **H:** 15-60 cm. **Hab:** Mossy heath and hillsides. Rare. **Sim:** None. **Fl:** May-June. **I:** Blátoppa. (Grass family).

Spikelet (m. 5)

299 Meadow Foxtail
Alopecurus pratensis

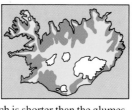

Spikelets single-flowered, close together in cylindrical, grey, 3-8 cm long and 6-10 mm broad spike, which on closer examination turns out to be a panicle, since the spikelets have very short branched pedicels. Spikelets with awn which is shorter than the glumes. Stamens hang out of the spike at flowering time, with violet or brown anthers. Culm round. Ligule 2-3 mm long, truncate but jagged. Leaves flat, 5-9 mm broad. **H:** 30-120 cm. **Hab:** Cultivated homefields, grassland. Foreign species which has for a long time been cultivated in homefields, and is now naturalized in grassland, and along edges of ditches and roads. Common. **Sim:** Marsh Foxtail (see 300). Timothy (302). The Meadow Foxtail differs through the glumes (see drawing); spikelets more loosely attached to the inflorescence axis. **Fl:** June-July. **I:** Hálíðagras. (Grass family).

Spikelet (m. 5)

300 Marsh Foxtail
Alopecurus geniculatus

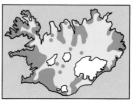

Spikelets single-flowered, close together in cylindrical, 2-3 cm long and 4-5 mm broad, dark grey and greyish violet terminal compound spike. One pistil with bifid stigma. Stamens three, anthers violet, hanging out of the spike at flowering time. Spikelet with knee-bent awn, which is much longer than the glume. Culm round, oblique or almost horizontal below; the uppermost knee bent, stretching the uppermost internode to upright position. Sheaths inflated; ligule about 2 mm long. **H:** 12-25 cm. **Hab:** Damp grassland, river banks and poorly drained homefields. Widespread, more common in the South. **Sim:** Orange Foxtail (301). The Marsh Foxtail differs through longer awns, far exceeding the spikelet, and through inflated sheaths. Meadow Foxtail (299). The Marsh Foxtail is much lower, with darker, shorter spike. **Fl:** June-August. **I:** Knjáliðagras. (Grass family).

Spikelet (m. 6)

301 Orange Foxtail
Alopecurus aequalis

Spikelets single-flowered, densely packed in cylindrical, light greyish green, 1.5-2 cm long terminal spike. Glumes green, dark-tipped, with white, erect hairs. Lemma with dorsal awn, projecting slightly above spikelet. Stamens hang out of spike at flowering time. Anthers yellow or rusty brown. Ligule 2-3 mm long. Leaves 2-4 mm broad, sharply ribbed on top, the broader leaves with 12-20 ribs. **H:** 10-30 cm; floating shoots often much longer. **Hab:** Muddy bottom of shallow lakes, ponds or marshland, calm streams and dikes. Widespread. **Sim:** Marsh Foxtail (see 300). **Fl:** July-August. **I:** Vatnsliðagras. (Grass family).

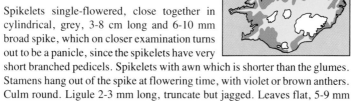

Spikelet (m. 8)

248

302 Timothy

Phleum pratense

Spikelets single-flowered, densely packed in cylindrical, 3-8 cm long, 8-12 mm broad, greyish green compound spike. Glumes 4-7 mm long, with long hairs on the keel; tapering abruptly towards a 1-3 mm long point. Lemma 2-3 mm long. Anthers violet, hanging out of spike at flowering time. Leaves rather broad, 4-8 mm; ligule 2-4 mm. **H:** 30-100 cm. **Hab:** Cultivated homefields and seeded grasslands; naturalized around farms. Common. **Sim:** Meadow Foxtail (see 299). **Fl:** June-July. **I:** Vallarfoxgras. (Grass family).

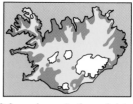
Spikelet (m. 8)

303 Alpine Cat's-tail
Phleum alpinum

Spikelets single-flowered, densely packed in cylindrical, dark, 1-3 cm long, 8-12 mm broad compound spike. Glumes 5-7 mm long, hairy on the keel; extended to sharp point which may be half of the total glume length or more. Ligule short, 1-2 mm. Uppermost leaf sheath inflated. Leaves 3-6 mm broad. **H:** 15-40 cm. **Hab:** Fertile, grassy hollows and slopes, ravines. Common, esp. at higher altitudes. **Sim:** Timothy (302). Alpine Cat's-tail differs through the inflated sheath, and shorter spike. **Fl:** June. **I:** Fjallafoxgras. (Grass family).

Spikelet (m. 6)

304 Bearded Couch
Elymus caninus

Tall grass with 6-12 cm long, green or slightly violet-tinted spike. Spikelets usually three-flowered, the top flower sterile. Glumes 10-20 mm long, lanceolate with long terminal awn, sparsely short-haired, with three to six raised nerves. Lemma with awn that is considerably longer than lemma itself. Leaves broad, 4-10 mm, hairy on top; ligule absent. **H:** 40-90 cm. **Sim:** Northern Couch (305). The Bearded Couch differs through the glumes and longer awns. **Hab:** Woodland and dwarf-shrub heath. Rare. **Fl:** July. **I:** Kjarrhveiti. (Grass family).

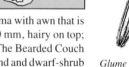
Glume (m. 2.6)

305 Northern Couch
Elymus alaskanus

Average-sized grass with 4-8 cm long spike, usually reddish violet. Spikelets with 3-4 flowers. Glumes green or purplish in the centre with broad membranous margin, sharp-pointed, usually oblique: Four nerves on one side and two or three on other side of middle nerve. Lemma hairy, with short awn. Leaves 3-5 mm broad, ligule absent. **H:** 25-40 cm. **Hab:** Dry gravelly hillsides and heathland. Rare. **Sim:** Bearded Couch (see 304). Common Couch (see 307). **Fl:** July. **I:** Bláhveiti. (Grass family).

Glume (m. 4)

306 Lyme-grass
Leymus arenarius

Tall, very coarse grass with 12-20 cm long and 10-18 mm broad terminal spike. Spikelets usually three-flowered, sometimes with a fourth sterile flower. Glumes lanceolate, pointed, 15-20 mm long, often slightly hairy. Lemma densely haired; the lowest of same length as glumes, the upper shorter, pointed, awnless. Anthers violet, about 5 mm long. Culms very sturdy, glabrous. Leaves 5-10 mm broad, the sides curving inwards in dry weather; shoot leaves usually narrower. **H:** 50-90 cm. **Hab:** Sand, esp. drifting sand, sandy lava fields and seashores. **Sim:** American Lyme-grass (see 306A). **Fl:** June. **I:** Melgresi. (Grass family). — **American Lyme-grass** *Leymus mollis* is closely related to the Common Lyme-grass, but the upper part of the culm is hairy. It has been sown in Iceland for soil reclamation; very rare.

Spikelet (m. 1.4)

307 Common Couch
Elymus repens

Tall grass with 8-15 mm long, green, terminal spike. Spikelets three- to five-flowered; glumes pointed, four to five-nerved, 7-10 mm long, lanceolate. Lemma 12-18 mm long, with awn that is less than half as long. Leaves 5-9 mm broad; no ligule. Creeps by means of strong, white, underground stolons. **H:** 40-80 cm. **Hab:** Around farms, unkept gardens and dumps. Common. **Sim:** Bearded Couch and Northern Couch (304, 305). The Common Couch differs through the long, branching underground stolons and short awn. Glumes pointed but awnless. **Fl:** June-July. **I:** Húsapuntur. (Grass family). — The dense leaf shoots rising from the underground runners make the couch a difficult weed in gardens once established.

Spikelet (m. 2.5)

308 Mat-grass
Nardus stricta

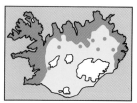

Grows in dense tufts. Flowers in blue, one-sided, quite narrow, 3-5 cm long terminal spike. Spikelets single-flowered, sessile. Glumes absent or very small. Lemma stiff, bluish, sharp-pointed, 7-10 mm long. Leaves in dense, stiff tussocks, filiform (0.5-1 mm), furrowed, rough, with upwards-directed points, and light brown, dense, 2-3 cm long sheaths at the base. **H:** 12-30 cm. **Hab:** Deep depressions and grassy hollows with moderate snow cover in winter. Common. **Sim:** None, easily distinguished by the slender, one-sided spike. **Fl:** June-July. **I:** Finnungur. (Grass family).

Spikelets (m. 2.5)

309 Marsh Arrowgrass
Triglochin palustris

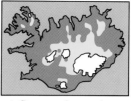

Perennial with slender (1-1.5 mm) stem, terminating in thin-flowered, 3-10 cm long raceme, still longer in fruit. Flowers short-stalked with six-leaved perianth. Perianth leaves purplish brown with greenish midrib, blunt. Stamens six, nearly sessile. Single pistil with hair-like terminal stigma which becomes an 8-9 mm long and 1.5 mm broad, trimerous fruit. Leaves linear, nearly round, green or flushed with red, with peculiar taste. **H:** 12-25 cm. **Hab:** Damp, open soil or bogs. Common. **Sim:** Sea Arrowgrass (310). The Marsh Arrowgrass is much more delicate, mature fruits more elongated, and fruit stalks appressed. **Fl:** June. **I:** Mýrasauðlaukur. (Arrowgrass family).

Fruit (m. 3)

310 Sea Arrowgrass
Triglochin maritima

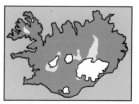

Perennial with rather stout stem, 2-2.5 mm thick. Flowers on short pedicels, 6-parted, in rather dense, long raceme. Perianth leaves blunt, purplish towards the margin, with green midrib. Stamens six, on very short filaments. Pistil maturing into a 4-5 mm long, six-merous fruit, 2.5 mm wide. Leaves linear, nearly round, greenish, strong, with same taste as Marsh Arrowgrass. **H:** 15-40 cm. **Hab:** Saltmarshes and sandy meadows near the sea. Fairly widespread. **Sim:** Marsh Arrowgrass (see 309). **Fl:** June. **I:** Strandsauðlaukur. (Arrow-grass family).

Fruit (m. 4.5)

311 Scheuchzer's Cottongrass
Eriophorum scheuchzeri

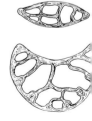

Flowers in one, short, terminal spike surrounded by a few membranous bracts; bracts transparent in lower part, dark brown above, pointed. Three stamens. Anthers yellow, short (1-2 mm). Pistil with long style and trifid stigma. Flowers surrounded by white hairs instead of perianth; the hairs first short, getting very long (2-3 cm) when fruit matures. Stem rotund; leaves narrow (1-2 mm), thick and channelled in lower part, extending into a flat tip. **H:** 20-30 cm. **Hab:** Roadside ditches, open peat-soil, sandy riversides, springs and bogs. Common. **Sim:** Common Cottongrass (338). The Scheuchzer's Cottongrass differs in its single spike, narrower leaves with flat, not triangular, point. **Fl:** May-June. **I:** Hrafnafífa. (Sedge family).

Section of leaf: point, base (m. 10)

312 Bellard's Kobresia
Kobresia myosuroides

Densely tufted, grass-like plant with 3 cm long basal sheaths. Flowers without perianth, in 1.5-2 cm long terminal spike; one male and one female flower in each spikelet. Scales light brown, with broad membranous margin above. Stamens three, one pistil with three stigmas. Fruit light brown, shiny, short-beaked. Leaves filiform, 0.5 mm wide, rotund, channelled. **H:** 15-30 cm. **Hab:** Dry hummocks and hill-tops, esp. in dry, exposed places with thin or no snow cover. Common. **Sim:** None. **Fl:** June. **I:** Þursaskegg. (Sedge family).

Fruit (m. 10)

313 Needle Spike-rush
Eleocharis acicularis

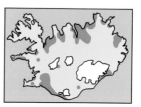

Very small, grass-like plant with filiform, 2-3 cm long and 0.2 mm broad, basal leaves. Only one, tiny, about 2 mm long, usually two-flowered terminal spike. Scales reddish brown to dark brown, with membranous margin and green midrib. Perianth leaves of similar type. Three stamens, one pistil with three stigmas. **H:** 2-5 cm. **Hab:** Mud in shallow ponds and lake inlets, shallow, muddy marshland. Rather widespread. **Sim:** Few-flowered Spike-rush (315). The Needle Spike-rush is much more delicate with a smaller spike. Awlwort (137) resembles Needle Spike-rush when not in flower, but has broader and more rigid leaves. **Fl:** August-Sept. **I:** Efjuskúfur. (Sedge family).

Spike (m. 10)

314 Common Spike-rush
Eleocharis palustris

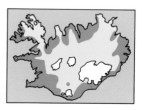

Rather large plant with 1-1.8 cm long, brown to reddish brown terminal spike. Two blunt scales below the spike, with membranous margin and green midrib, each clasping about half the stem. Bracts pointed, reddish brown. Six tiny bristles instead of perianth. Pistil beaked with two stigmas. Six stamens. Culm rotund, hollow, with blade-less brown-edged sheaths near the base. **H:** 20-70 cm. **Hab:** Lakes inlets, ponds and dikes with shallow water. Common. **Sim:** Slender Spike-rush (see 314A). **Fl:** June-July. **I:** Vatnsnál. (Sedge family). — **Slender Spike-rush** *Eleocharis uniglumis* resembles Common Spike-rush, but is generally found in bogs, esp. near the sea. It is usually smaller, with a shorter spike; it is best distinguished by the lower scale, which encircles the stem completely, whereas on Common Spike-rush it clasps only half the stem against the upper scale.

Spike (m. 2.8)

315 Few-flowered Spike-rush
■□
□□
Eleocharis quinqueflora

Single, very short (5-7 mm), dark brown, terminal spike. Scales dark brown, ovate, pointed, with broad membranous margin. Six bristles replace the perianth. Three stamens, pistil with three stigmas. Fruit a small, three-sided yellowish nutlet, about 2 mm long. Stem leafless, with reddish brown sheaths in the lower part. Leaves basal, rotund, striate. **H:** 5-18 cm. **Hab:** Moist soil on stream banks, rock ledges, shallow bogs on bedrock. **Sim:** Three-flowered Rush (see 317). Few-flowered Spike-rush differs in the bladeless sheaths, and six bristles around the fruit. **Fl:** May-June. **I:** Fitjaskúfur. (Sedge family).

Sheath on stem (m. 3.5)

316 Deergrass
□■
□□
Trichophorum caespitosum

Grows in dense tufts. Spike 4-5 mm, light brown, few-flowered. Glumes slightly shorter than spike, with a broad membranous margin below, and a blunt, often greenish terminal point. Three stamens, pistil with three stigmas. Stem often curved, with a 4-6 mm long, greenish leaf stump in the lower part. **H:** 8-20 cm. **Hab:** Bogs, esp. in coastal areas. Common. **Sim:** None; differs from Few-flowered Spike-rush (315) in the smaller and lighter spikes, and the very short leaf tip of the stem sheaths. **Fl:** May-June. **I:** Mýrafinnungur. (Sedge family).

Sheath on stem (m. 3.5)

317 Three-flowered Rush
□□
■□
Juncus triglumis

One small, terminal group of three or four flowers, surrounded by brownish scale leaves. Perianth leaves six, yellowish white or pinkish with darker tip. Stamens six; single pistil with trifid stigma. Fruit dark reddish brown. Leaves near the base, rotund. **H:** 5-18 cm. **Hab:** Moist, open soil or boggy ground on bedrock. Common. **Sim:** Two-flowered Rush (see 318). Few-flowered Spike-rush (see 315). **Fl:** June. **I:** Blómsef. (Rush family).

Cluster of flowers (m. 4)

318 Two-flowered Rush
□□
□■
Juncus biglumis

Usually two flowers on top of culm. Bract short, slightly longer than the inflorescence. Perianth leaves six, dark brown, pointed. Stamens six, one pistil with trifid stigma. Fruit yellowish, often dark brown at the top and edges, blunt or slightly indented. Leaves only near base, slender, rotund, pointed. **H:** 4-15 cm. **Hab:** Moist, open soil, more frequent in the mountains. Common. **Sim:** Three-flowered Rush (317). Two-flowered Rush differs by longer bract, fewer flowers, colour of perianth and shape of fruit. **Fl:** June. **I:** Flagasef. (Rush family).

Cluster of flowers (m. 2.8)

319 Dioecious Sedge
■■
□□
Carex dioeca

Small sedge with single, short, terminal unisexual spike; female spike (left) usually 1 cm
long or less, thicker than the male spike (right),
which is slightly longer, 1-1.5 cm. Scales of
female flowers rather broad, acute, shiny, membranous, brown. Utricle
brown, beaked. Two stigmas. Scales of male flowers light brown. Culms
round, leaves narrow (1 mm), channelled below, tapering to a flat point. **H:**
8-18 cm. **Hab:** Damp soil and bogs. Widespread. **Sim:** Easily identified as the
only dioecious sedge in Iceland. Similar to immature Bristle Sedge (see 321).
Fl: June. **I:** Sérbýlisstör. (Sedge family).

*Utricle
(m. 10)*

320 Rock Sedge
□□
■□
Carex rupestris

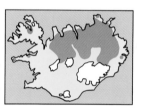

Single, short (8-15 mm), terminal spike with
male flowers at the top, females underneath.
Scales membranous, dark brown, broadly
ovate or nearly round. Utricle dully triangular,
brown, with very short beak, shiny, veined. Three stigmas. Grows in rather
dense, curly tufts with irregularly curved, 1-2 mm broad, rough-edged leaves,
channelled near the base, triangular towards the tip; old, dead leaves from previous years usually abundantly present. **H:** 6-18 cm. **Hab:** Dry hummocks
and hilltops. Common in the interior of N and E Iceland, rare elsewhere. **Sim:**
Glacier Sedge (329) selects similar habitats. The Rock Sedge is coarser with
curved leaves and single spike; the Glacier Sedge has several close spikes. **Fl:**
May-June. **I:** Móastör. (Sedge family).

*Utricle
(m. 11)*

321 Bristle Sedge
□□
□■
Carex microglochin

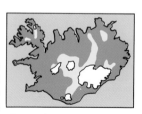

Small sedge with short, terminal spike. The
spike with distinct bristles, directed upwards
while young, later pointing down. Female
scales broad, dull-pointed, ovate. Stigmas
three. Utricle long (6-10 mm) and narrow, rotund, tapering upwards. Green
bristle grows up through the utricle at the side of the stigmas, later turning
down. Mature spike therefore with many, sharp-pointed, bent-down bristles.
Culm rotund, striate, leaves slender, nearly round, channelled near the base.
H: 5-20 cm. **Hab:** Sandy banks, riversides, frequently in shallow moist soil
over bedrock or in bogs. Common. **Sim:** Dioecious Sedge (319) or Few-flowered Spike-rush (315) before and Flea Sedge (see 322) after the utricles have
been directed downwards. The Bristle Sedge differs by the bristle growing out
of the utricle. **Fl:** June. **I:** Broddastör. (Sedge family).

*Utricle
(m. 7.5)*

322 Flea Sedge
■□
□□
Carex pulicaris

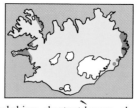

Comparatively small sedge with one rather lax
terminal spike; female flowers below, male
flowers above. The fruits deflexed at maturity.
Scales pointed, light brown, membranous.
Utricle slender, rather long, 4-5 mm, smooth and shiny, chestnut-brown, elliptic to lanceolate, falling off early at maturity. Stigmas two. Culms round,
striate. Leaves slender (1 mm), channelled. **H:** 15-20 cm. **Hab:** Moist soil.
Rare. **Sim:** Bristle Sedge (see 321). **Fl:** July. **I:** Hagastör. (Sedge family).

Utricle
(m. 6)

323 Nard Sedge
□■
□□
Carex nardina

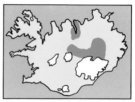

Very small sedge, usually with one short spike,
rarely two; male flowers at top. Scales light
brown, membranous; utricle light brown, tapering to a beak. Two stigmas. Culms round.
Leaves filiform, round and channelled below with triangular tip, of similar
length or slightly longer than the spike. Grows in dense tufts with curved
leaves and culms. **H:** 3-8 cm. **Hab:** Gravelly soil at high altitudes. Rare. **Sim:**
Recalls small Kobresia (312) when not in flower. **Fl:** July. **I:** Finnungsstör.
(Sedge family).

Utricle
(m. 8)

324 Capitate Sedge
□□
■□
Carex capitata

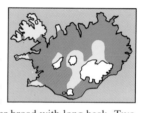

Tufted sedge of average size. Spike short, almost globose, 6-8 mm long and 6-7 mm wide.
Male flowers form small beak at the top, female
flowers in the wider base. Scales brown in the
centre, with membranous margin. Utricle rather broad with long beak. Two
stigmas. Leaves slender (1 mm) with rough edges, appearing round, but in
fact deeply channelled or folded lengthwise. **H:** 15-30 cm. **Hab:** Dry, grassy
ground or heath. Common. **Sim:** None. **Fl:** June. **I:** Hnappstör. (Sedge family).

Utricle
(m. 7.5)

325 Thick-headed Sedge
□□
□■
Carex macloviana

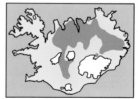

Average-sized sedge with several, small,
closely tufted spikes forming dense, conical
terminal head, 10-15 mm long and 8-12 mm
wide. Scales dark brown, with membranous
margin, acute. Utricle with toothed beak, tapering upwards. Two stigmas.
Leaves flat, 2-3 mm broad, rough-edged, shiny. Culm triangular above, furrowed. **H:**15-30 cm. **Hab:** Grassland and grassy patches in heathland. Rare.
Sim: Rather easily distinguished by the dark brown, shiny spike heads. **Fl:**
July. **I:** Kollstör. (Sedge family).

Utricle
(m. 6.5)

326 Curved Sedge
Carex maritima

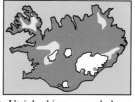

Rather low sedge, with several, densely tufted spikes in compact, conical head (1.5x1 cm). Male flowers at the top, and female flowers in lower part of spikelets. Scales brown, membranous, with distinct midrib extended to a point. Utricle shiny, green below, brown above, with long, tapering beak. Two stigmas. Culm nearly round, usually curved down. Leaves narrow, 1-1.5 mm, channelled near base, with three-sided tip. Forms very long, branched, underground runners, esp. when growing in sand. **H:** 8-20 cm. **Hab:** Damp, sandy riversides and banks, moderately moist sand near the seashore and in the interior deserts. Widespread. **Sim:** None. **Fl:** June. **I:** Bjúgstör. (Sedge family).

Utricle (m. 6)

327 String Sedge
Carex chordorrhiza

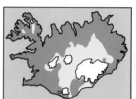

Sedge of average size, with ascending, usually inclined culms, and several closely tufted terminal spikes. Spikes tipped with male flowers, female flowers underneath. Scales long, pointed, brown, with membranous margin. Utricle light green to light brown, striate. Two stigmas. Culms rather sturdy, nearly round, inclined. Leaves flat or keeled, 2 mm broad. Long, decumbent leaf shoots lie above ground becoming up to 60 cm long or more in the fall (termed "winter anxiety" in Icelandic because of the former belief that long String Sedge shoots boded a hard winter). **H:** 15-30 cm. **Hab:** Wet bogs, marshland and quagmires. Common. **Sim:** None, differs from other sedges by the inclined culms and the long, loose-lying leaf shoots. **Fl:** June. **I:** Vetrarkvíðastör. (Sedge family).

Utricle (m. 8.5)

328 Pill Sedge
Carex pilulifera

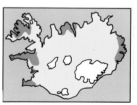

Sedge of moderate size with slender, limp stems. Two or three rather close female spikes, one terminal male spike. Bract of lowest spike leaf-like, 5-15 mm long. Scales tawny; the midrib extended to a point. Utricle hairy, swollen, beaked. Three stigmas. Culms very slender (1 mm), triangular at the top, lengthening and hanging down late in the summer. Leaves flat or keeled, with revolute edges, 1.5-3.5 mm broad. **H:** 15-35 cm. **Hab:** Dry grassland and grassy hillsides. Widespread in some districts. **Sim:** None, except Spring Sedge (328A). **Fl:** July. **I:** Dúnhulstrastör. (Sedge family). — **Spring Sedge** *Carex caryophyllea* is a very rare sedge, resembling Pill Sedge in having hairy utricles. The culms are much stiffer, spikes longer, and scales green around the midrib. Found only in the southern slope of Reykjanes Peninsula.

Utricle (m. 11)

329 Glacier Sedge
Carex glacialis

Very small sedge with short terminal male spike, and several, few-flowered, close female spikes. Scales brownish with broad membranous margin. Utricle variegated, green and brownish, shiny, swollen, with rather long beak. Three stigmas. Grows in small, dense tufts. Culms short, round. Leaves densely tufted, 1 mm broad, channelled or keeled, with rough edges and triangular tips. **H:** 4-8 cm. **Hab:** On dry soil, hilltops, rock outcrops, mountain edges and other exposed locations. Common in N and NE Iceland, very rare elsewhere. **Sim:** Easily distinguished in flower, but the habitat and the leaf tufts recall the Alpine Rock Sedge (320). The Glacier Sedge differs in its many spikes and shorter, straight leaf tufts. **Fl:** June-July. **I:** Dvergstör. (Sedge family).

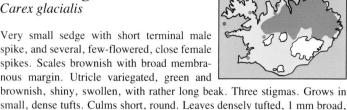

Utricle (m. 14)

330 Close-headed Alpine-Sedge
Carex norvegica

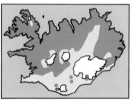

Straight, upright sedge, usually with three, sessile, close spikes. The top spike larger, with male flowers at the base. Scales dark brown or black, pointed. Utricles brown, with rough or even bristly surface, acute or short-beaked; three stigmas. Culms triangular. Leaves 1.5-3 cm, keeled or flat, with rough edges. **H:** 15-30 cm. **Hab:** Heathland and pastures. Common, but very scattered. **Sim:** Black Alpine-sedge (331). The Close-headed Alpine-Sedge has very short-stalked spikes and narrower leaves; the top straight, never nodding. **Fl:** June-July. **I:** Fjallastör. (Sedge family).

Utricle (m. 12)

331 Black Alpine-sedge
Carex atrata

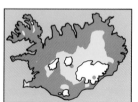

Spikes usually four to five, stalked, slightly drooping. Male flowers basal in the top spike. Scales black or sooty red. Utricle green, three stigmas. Culms sharply triangular, thick below, slender and slightly nodding at top. Leaf shoots sturdy. Leaves flat with recurved edge, 4-6 mm broad. **H:** 25-50 cm. **Hab:** Slopes, grassy ravines, rock ledges or heathland. Rather common, but usually scattered. **Sim:** Close-headed Alpine-sedge (see 330). Stiff Sedge (352) has similar female spikes and leaves. The Black Alpine-sedge differs in lacking the terminal male spike. **Fl:** June-July. **I:** Sótstör. (Sedge family). **Club Sedge** *Carex buxbaumi* is a rare sedge, resembling Black Alpine-sedge in having male flowers basal in the top spike, but the other spikes are more spreading and upright, utricle green, scales long and pointed.

Utricle (m. 9)

332 Bicoloured Sedge
Carex bicolor

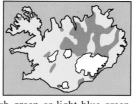

Usually two or three ovate to roundish spikes; culms slender, drooping or lying limp on the ground. Male flowers at the base of the top spike. Scales dark brown, blunt, often with green midrib. Utricle obovate, beakless, whitish green or light blue-green with rough surface. Two stamens. Leaves 1.5-2.5 mm, flat or slightly keeled, often with revolute margin. **H:** Culm 10-25 cm long, usually lying on the ground when fruit is mature. **Hab:** Damp, open soil, banks and riversides. Rather rare. **Sim:** Red Sedge (333). The Bicoloured Sedge differs in lighter utricles, longer, decumbent culms. **Fl:** June-July. **I:** Hvítstör. (Sedge family).

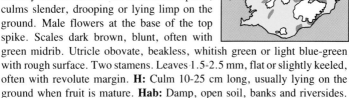

Utricle (m. 17)

333 Red Sedge
Carex rufina

Small, leafy mountain sedge. Three to five, rather close, short-stalked or sessile spikes, all with female flowers; male flowers only at the base of the top spike. Scales rather short, dark reddish brown or black, usually with green midrib. Utricles green, short-beaked; two stigmas. Leaves in dense tufts, longer than the culms, 1-2 mm broad, usually keeled, with triangular tip. **H:** 5-15 cm. **Hab:** Bog edges, moist soil along water courses and riversides; frequently near pond and lake margins or at the edge of dried-up ponds. Widespread throughout the Central Highlands, sometimes also in coastal mountains. **Sim:** Bicoloured Sedge (see 332). The Red Sedge differs in that the culms are much shorter than the leaves. **Fl:** July-August. **I:** Rauðstör. (Sedge family).

Utricle (m. 12)

334 Star Sedge
Carex echinata

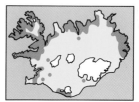

Usually three to four globose spikes with short intervals at top of culm. Male flowers at base of terminal spike. Scales light brown, with membranous margin, usually with green midrib. Utricle 3-4 mm long, brownish or greenish, with long, flat, rough-edged beak, with divided top. Two stigmas. Culms dull triangular, striate near top. Leaves 1.5-3 mm broad, flat or keeled, smooth. **H:** 15-30 cm. **Hab:** Moist creek banks, sloping bogs, near springs. Common in coastal areas. **Sim:** None. **Fl:** July. **I:** Ígulstör. (Sedge family). — **Lesser Tussock-sedge** *Carex diandra* is a rather large, rare sedge whose inflorescence recalls Star Sedge in having sessile spikes with short intervals at the top of stem. It differs in its dark brown colour. Grows in bogs and marshland.

Utricle (m. 9)

268

335 Hare's-foot Sedge
Carex lachenalii

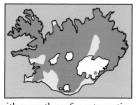

Three to four spikes on top of stem, the terminal spike larger than the others; male flowers at base of all spikes. Scales light brown, ovate, blunt, with membranous margin. Utricle tapers to a beak, yellowish green or yellowish brown, with smooth surface; two stigmas. Culms in dense tufts, triangular. Leaves 1.5-2.5 mm broad, flat, with rough edges; leaf shoots inclined. **H:** 12-30 cm. **Hab:** Moist snowbeds, stream-banks and ravines in the mountains. Common. **Sim:** Gravel Sedge (see 335A). **Fl:** June-July. **I:** Rjúpustör. (Sedge family). — **Gravel Sedge** *Carex glareosa* resembles Hare's-foot Sedge, but grows almost exclusively on moist, often sandy banks near the seashore. It has longer, more slender, limp culms, that lie flat on the ground when the fruits are mature. Utricles with distinct, raised nerves. — **Hudson Bay Sedge** *Carex heleonastes* is a very rare sedge, resembling Hare's-foot Sedge, but taller with darker, thicker and more globose spikes; culms are scattered and not tufted; grows in wet bogs in the interior of the North.

Utricle (m. 14)

336 Norway Sedge
Carex mackenziei

Three to five spikes at the top of stem; male flowers at the base of the large terminal spike. Scales long, usually longer than utricle, ovate, dull-pointed or blunt, yellowish tawny with green midrib. Utricle short, swollen, short-beaked, with many raised veins. Stigmas two. Long, creeping stolons with rather long, light green shoots, forming dense, limp patches; leaves 2-3.5 mm broad, flat. **H:** 15-40 cm. **Hab:** Saltmarshes and bogs flooded at spring-tides. Fairly widespread along the coast except in the South. **Sim:** The spikes resemble Hare's-foot Sedge (335), or White Sedge (337); the terminal spike is longer on the Norway Sedge, and has a narrower base. **Fl:** June-July. **I:** Skriðstör. (Sedge family).

Utricle (m. 12)

337 White Sedge
Carex curta

Grows in dense, rather large tufts; 4-7 obovate, oblong, light greyish green spikes, somewhat spread out on the culms. Few male flowers at base of spikes. Scales light green, membranous, pointed. Utricle light yellowish green, tapering to a point; stigmas two. Culms sharply triangular. Leaves flat, 1.5-3.5 cm broad. **H:** 20-50 cm. **Hab:** Bogs, lake banks and pond edges. Common. **Sim:** Brownish Sedge (see 337A). **Fl:** June-July. **I:** Blátoppastör. (Sedge family). — **Brownish Sedge** *Carex brunnescens* is a rare sedge resembling White Sedge, with lighter brown-tinted, almost globose spikes, and slender culms; grows in grassland.

Utricle (m. 12)

270

338 Common Cottongrass

Eriophorum angustifolium

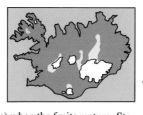

Flowers in 4-6 stalked, drooping spikes at the side of rather long, green bract. Scales membranous and transparent below, greyish brown above. Florets surrounded by white hairs instead of perianth; the hairs get very long (2-3 cm) when the fruits mature. Stamens three; anthers long (4-5 mm), yellow. Single pistil with long, trifid stigma in each flower. Stem round. Leaves 4-8 mm broad, flat or keeled near base, sharply triangular in upper part. **H:** 20-40 cm. **Hab:** Bogs, mires and moist lakebanks. Very common. **Sim:** Scheuchzer's Cottongrass (311). The Common Cottongrass differs in having many spikes, broader leaves with triangular tips. **Fl:** June. **I:** Klófífa. (Sedge family).

Section of leaf: point, base (m. 6)

339 Hair Sedge

Carex capillaris

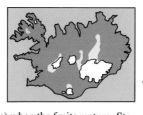

Small sedge with two or three female spikes hanging on long, slender stalks. One small male spike. Scales light brown with whitish, membranous, worn edges. Utricle light brown or greenish, with rather long beak, shiny, 3 mm long. Three stigmas. Culms dully triangular, striate. Leaves flat, 1-2 mm broad below, the tip triangular. **H:** 8-25 cm. **Hab:** Damp soil in heathland and pastures. Common. **Sim:** Porsild's Sedge (see 339A). **Fl:** June. **I:** Hárleggjastör. (Sedge family). — **Porsild's Sedge** *Carex krausei* is closely related to Hair Sedge, but has female flowers in the upper part of the terminal spike besides the male flowers; female spikes more upright and brownish, at longer intervals on the stem. Rather common in the interior of N and NE Iceland.

Utricle (m. 12)

340 Sheathed Sedge
Carex vaginata

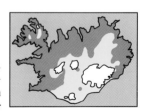

Average-sized sedge, with two or three, stalked, upright female spikes, and one terminal male spike. Scales short-pointed, brownish with green midrib, membranous. Utricle rather large, 4 mm, green, with short, often oblique beak. Three stigmas. Culms dully triangular, striate. Leaves broad, 3-5.5 mm, bright green, flat or M-shaped. Bract sheaths long, 10-20 mm. **H:** 20-45 cm. **Hab:** Woodland, dwarf-shrub heaths, sheltered dells and slopes, dry grassland. Common, esp. in the North. **Sim:** Carnation Sedge (341). The Sheathed Sedge has brighter green leaves, lighter utricles, growing in drier soil than the Carnation Sedge, which is always bluish green. **Fl:** May-June. **I:** Slíðrastör. (Sedge family).

Utricle (m. 8)

341 Carnation Sedge
■□
□□
Carex panicea

Average-sized sedge with one to three, stalked, upright female spikes, and one terminal male spike. Scales light or dark brown, pointed, with narrow, whitish membranous margin. Utricle greenish brown or dark brown, 4-5 mm long, swollen, with oblique beak. Three stigmas. Leaves rather broad, 2.5-4 mm, bluish green; lowest bract with 10-20 mm long sheath. **H:** 15-35 cm. **Hab:** Moist heathland, damp open soil, bogs and creek banks. Common. **Sim:** Sheathed Sedge (see 340). The Carnation Sedge differs by the bluish green colour, and by darker, more inflated utricles. **Fl:** June-July. **I:** Belgjastör. (Sedge family).

Utricle (m. 8)

342 Livid Sedge
□■
□□
Carex livida

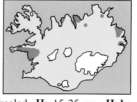

One or two upright, short-stalked, few-flowered female spikes, one terminal male spike. Scales brown with green midrib, blunt. Utricle light blue-green or yellowish green, usually beakless. Three stigmas. Leaves blue-green, keeled. **H:** 15-25 cm. **Hab:** Bogs and wet mires. Rare. **Sim:** Carnation Sedge (341). The Livid Sedge differs in its fewer and closer female flowers, and lighter coloured, beakless utricles. **Fl:** June-July. **I:** Fölvastör. (Sedge family).

Utricle (m. 7.5)

343 Glaucous Sedge
□□
■□
Carex flacca

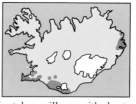

Rather large sedge with one or two terminal male spikes and two to four female spikes; the lower ones 2-3 cm long, on slender stalks. Scales dark greyish brown, often with greenish midrib. Utricle green or dark greyish brown, minutely papillose, with short, black beak. Three stigmas. Culm triangular. Leaves blue-green, flat with recurved edge, 3-5 mm broad. **H:** 25-45 cm. **Hab:** Grassy slopes, heathland and pastures. Scattered in the South. **Sim:** Sheathed Sedge (340) and Carnation Sedge (341). The Glaucous Sedge differs in its short (2-5 mm) bract sheaths, and longer, darker spikes. **Fl:** June-July. **I:** Grástör. (Sedge family).

Utricle (m. 8)

344 Tall Bog-sedge
□□
□■
Carex magellanica

Average-sized, green sedge with two or three, short, drooping, long-stalked female spikes and one upright male spike. Scales dark brown, long and narrowly pointed; the point usually curved, greatly exceeding the utricle which is green, often dark above, beakless, rough. Three stigmas. Culms triangular, slender. Leaves flat; the lowest bract exceeding the spikes. **H:** 15-30 cm. **Hab:** Wet bogs. Rather rare. **Sim:** Common Bog-sedge (see 345). **Fl:** June-July. **I:** Keldustör. (Sedge family).

Utricle (m. 8)

345 Common Bog-sedge
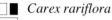
Carex limosa

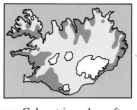

Average-sized sedge with one or two, rather large, drooping, long-stalked female spikes and one upright male spike. Scales light brown, pointed, with worn upper edge. Utricle light or yellowish brown, beakless, rough. Stigmas three. Culms triangular, often rough. Leaves rather narrow, 1.5-2 mm, bluish green, rather long, keeled or with recurved margin. **H:** 15-35 cm. **Hab:** Wet bogs. Rather common. **Sim:** Tall Bog Sedge (344). The Common Bog-sedge differs in shorter scales, longer female spikes; narrower, closer and more blue-green leaves. Mountain Bog-sedge (see 346). **Fl:** June-July. **I:** Flóastör. (Sedge family).

Utricle (m. 9)

346 Mountain Bog-sedge
Carex rariflora

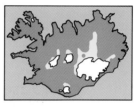

Rather small sedge, usually with two, drooping, long-stalked, 5-8-flowered, nearly black female spikes and one upright male spike. Scales pointed, dark brown or black with lighter midrib. Utricle light green, pointed but beakless, with rough surface. Stigmas three. Leaves 1.5-3 mm broad, flat, bluish green, usually short. **H:** 10-25 cm. **Hab:** Bogs and mires, esp. at higher altitudes. Common. **Sim:** Common Bog-sedge (345). The Mountain Bog-sedge differs in the darker, shorter female spikes with fewer flowers; also in the smaller size and shorter leaves. **Fl:** May-June. **I:** Hengistör. (Sedge family).

Utricle (m. 9)

347 Small-fruited Yellow-sedge
Carex serotina

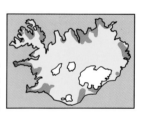

Small sedge with two or three, ovate to nearly globose, green female spikes which are very close, at least the two upper ones. One terminal male spike. Scales light yellowish green or yellowish brown, often bright green around the midrib, pointed. Utricle green or yellowish green, 2-2.5 mm long, distinctly veined, with very long beak. Three stigmas. Long bract below spikes, standing straight out or inclined downwards. Dense leaf shoots; leaves 1.5-3 mm broad, often flat. Culms triangular. **H:** 5-18 cm. **Hab:** Moist, boggy soil around lakes or in drained ponds; bogs and warm springs. **Sim:** Common Yellow-sedge and Large Yellow-sedge (see 347 A and B). **Fl:** June-July. **I:** Gullstör. — Yellow-sedge is very variable and has been divided into several closely related species. It is not definitely known which of these are present in Iceland. — **Common Yellow-sedge** *Carex demissa* is one of these species. It has a darker green and larger utricle (2.5-4 mm) than the Small-fruited Yellow-sedge and the culms are usually much longer than the basal leaves. Distribution in Iceland not known. — **Large Yellow-sedge** *Carex flava* is much taller and with larger spikes; the beak of the utricle longer and usually curved. Very rare in the North.

Utricle (m. 10)

348 Lyngbye's Sedge
■□
Carex lyngbyei

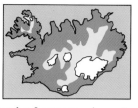

Large Sedge with two to four, drooping, long-stalked, 2-3 cm long female spikes and one or two upright male spikes. Scales dark brown, shiny, with long, acute point. Utricle elliptic, beakless, dull. Stigmas two. Culms sharply triangular. Leaves very large, 4-10 mm broad, with recurved edges, becoming yellowish green late in summer. Leaf sheaths usually reddish to reddish brown. **H:** 25-125 cm. **Hab:** Bogs, marshland and lake margins in the lowland, favouring iron-rich seepages and dikes in highland bogs. Common. **Sim:** None; see Saltmarsh Sedge (349). **Fl:** June. **I:** Gulstör. (Sedge family). — The Lyngbye's Sedge often dominates large areas in marshland along rivers and estuaries, formerly much harvested for hay. It is one of the few western species in Icelandic flora, unknown on the European continent.

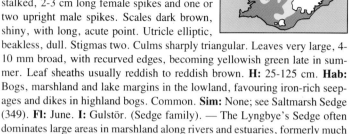

Utricle (m. 12)

349 Saltmarsh Sedge
□■
Carex salina

Average-sized sedge, with two to four, stalked, but nearly upright female spikes and one or two terminal male spikes. Scales pointed, dark brown with lighter midrib. Utricle ovate, beakless or short-beaked, veined. Leaves 2-5 mm broad, usually taller than the culms. **H:** 12-30 cm. **Hab:** Marshland in the uppermost zone reached by spring tides. Rather rare, but frequently dominating large areas. **Sim:** Lyngbye's Sedge (348). The Saltmarsh Sedge is much lower; differs in the leaves which exeed the culms, and the upright, short-stalked female spikes. **Fl:** June-July. **I:** Marstör. (Sedge family).

Utricle (m. 9)

350 Hoppner Sedge
□□
■
Carex subspathacea

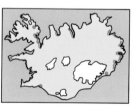

Very small sedge with long, creeping rootstocks. Usually two small, short-stalked, upright female spikes and one male spike. Scales reddish, green or black, often variegated, pointed. Utricle obovate, greenish with short beak. Two stigmas. Leaves of same length or longer than the culms, narrow (1-3 mm), channelled, usually curved backwards from the rather long sheaths, rarely flat or with recurved edges. **H:** 4-10 cm. **Hab:** Saltmarshes. Widespread along the coast. **Sim:** None. **Fl:** May-June. **I:** Flæðastör. (Sedge family). — The Hoppner Sedge often dominates large areas in the lower part of saltmarshes, forming dense covers of short leaf shoots. It flowers early and the fruits mature soon. No spikes are visible on the Hoppner Sedge in the saltmarshes late in summer after it has shed its seeds.

Utricle (m. 10)

351 Common Sedge
Carex nigra

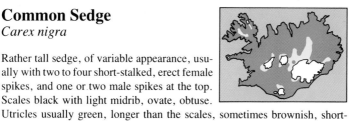

Rather tall sedge, of variable appearance, usually with two to four short-stalked, erect female spikes, and one or two male spikes at the top. Scales black with light midrib, ovate, obtuse. Utricles usually green, longer than the scales, sometimes brownish, short-beaked or beakless. Long bracts with very short green or light brown sheaths. Culms triangular, rather slender. Leaves long and narrow, 2-3 mm broad, keeled; leaf edge involute. **H:** 20-80 cm. **Hab:** Mires and lake margins. Very common. **Sim:** Stiff Sedge (see 352). **Fl:** June. **I:** Mýrastör. (Sedge family).

Utricle (m. 12)

352 Stiff Sedge
Carex bigelowii

Variable sedge of average size, usually with two, rarely three upright female spikes and one terminal male spike. Scales short, blunt, rarely pointed, often almost round, black with lighter midrib. Utricle green or nearly black, beakless or with short beak, not shiny. Bract sheaths very short, usually black. Strong, creeping rootstock with stiff, sharply triangular culms. Leaves broad, 2.5-5 mm, bright green or yellowish green; leaf edges usually revolute. **H:** 15-40 cm. **Hab:** Moderately dry heaths and moss-carpets; at higher altitudes sometimes in bogs. Very common. **Sim:** Common Sedge (351). The Stiff Sedge differs in the closer, fewer female spikes, down-rolled leaf margin, strong, curved stolons, darker utricles and black sheath of the lowest bract. **Fl:** June. **I:** Stinnastör. (Sedge family).

Utricle (m. 12)

353 Russet Sedge
Carex saxatilis

Average-sized sedge, usually with two, shiny, dark brown or brownish black female spikes and single, terminal male spike. Scales black including midrib. Utricles usually dark brown or black, rarely lighter brown below, shiny, beaked. Leaves channelled, 2-4 mm broad, edges involute. **H:** 15-35 cm. **Hab:** Bogs, sometimes stony or open soil, drained ponds or lake margins. Common, esp. at higher altitudes. **Sim:** None. **Fl:** June-July. **I:** Hrafnastör. (Sedge family). — **Pale Sedge** *Carex pallescens* is a rather tall sedge with green, stalked female spikes. Utricle shiny, light green, beakless. Only found in two localities in Iceland.

Utricle (m. 10)

354 Bottle Sedge
Carex rostrata

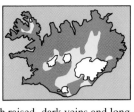

Very large, coarse-leaved sedge, with two to four stalked, upright, usually green or yellowish green female spikes, and two or three male spikes at the top. Scales pointed, lanceolate or ovate-lanceolate. Utricle light green, with raised, dark veins and long (1 mm) beak. Rhizome very strong with leafy shoots and sturdy culms. Leaves large, 4-7 mm broad, bluish green, V-shaped; sheaths of basal leaves light greyish brown. **H:** 30-100 cm. **Hab:** Ponds, inlets and margins of lakes, wet bogs at low and medium altitudes. Common. **Sim:** None. **Fl:** July. **I:** Tjarnastör. (Sedge family).

Utricle (m. 6)

355 Spiked Wood-rush
Luzula spicata

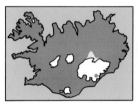

Several compact flower-clusters arranged in drooping, spike-like inflorescence at top of stem. Perianth leaves six, dark brown or nearly black, pointed. Stamens six. Pistil triangular, single-styled with trifid stigma. Lowest bract usually only half the length of inflorescence. Basal leaves narrow (1.5-2.5 mm), channelled, hairy on margin near base. **H:** 15-30 cm. **Hab:** Heathland, pastures, gravelly soil and mountain slopes. Very common. **Sim:** None. **Fl:** June. **I:** Axhæra. (Rush family).

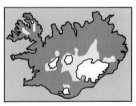

Fruit with perianth (m. 10)

356 Heath Wood-rush
Luzula multiflora

Many flowers in 4-8 compact, roundish clusters on stalks of variable length. Perianth leaves six, pointed, dark brown. Stamens six. Triangular, single-styled pistil with trifid stigma. Culm round. The bract usually extends up through the inflorescence. Basal leaves 3-6 mm broad, flat or with a slightly involute edge, usually more or less reddish with long, white marginal hairs at the base. **H:** 15-50 cm. **Hab:** Heathland, grassland, woodland and hillsides. Very common. **Sim:** Sudetan Wood-rush (356A). **Fl:** June. **I:** Vallhæra. (Rush family). —**Sudetan Wood-rush** *Luzula sudetica* is closely related to Heath Wood-rush, and not always separated from that species. The flower clusters are darker, usually staying very close, the upper part of the plant is more red, the culm ascending at the base. Grows in wetter habitats.

Fruit with perianth (m. 10)

357 Curved Wood-rush

Luzula arcuata

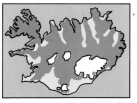

Several flowers together in 2-7 compact, roundish clusters on very slender, often curved stalks of variable length. Perianth leaves six, dark brown, membranous, sharply pointed. Stamens six. One-styled pistil with trifid stigma. Culm round. Bract usually very short, at most 5-10 mm. Basal leaves channelled, 1-2 mm broad, sharply pointed, usually with several long, white hairs at the base. **H:** 5-15 cm. **Hab:** Open soil, mountain heaths and rock outcrops. Common above 6-700 m. **Sim:** Heath Wood-rush (356). The Curved Wood-rush differs in the slender stalks of the flower clusters, and in narrower basal leaves. **Fl:** June-July. **I:** Fjallhæra. (Rush family). — The number of flower-clusters is very variable on the Curved Wood-rush. Ssp. *confusa* (often regarded a separate species) has a rather large, terminal cluster and one or few, long-stalked lateral flower-clusters. Ssp. *arcuata* on the other hand has numerous, small, long-stalked, curved flower-clusters. It is much more common than ssp. *confusa*. The separation of these two subspecies is often quite indistinct.

Fruit with perianth (m. 8)

358 Alpine Rush

Juncus alpinus

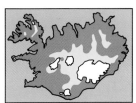

Several flowers together in 3-10 compact clusters on erect stalks of variable length. Perianth leaves six, dark brown, sharp-pointed, 2-3.5 mm long. Stamens six, with light yellow anthers. Pistil with three stigmas. Fruit brown, at least the top, shiny. Leaves round, 1-1.5 mm wide, hollow, with cross-walls easily felt if the leaves are stroked lengthwise. **H:** 10-35 cm. **Hab:** Moist, open soil, disused ditches, bogs. Common. **Sim:** Jointed Rush (359). The Alpine Rush differs in its smaller flower-clusters, more upright, slender stalks, narrower culms and leaves. **Fl:** June-July. **I:** Mýrasef. (Rush family).

Inflorescence (1:1)

359 Jointed Rush

Juncus articulatus

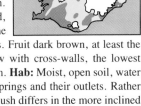

Several flowers together in 3-10, compact clusters on inclined stalks of variable length. Perianth 6-leaved, the leaves sharp-pointed, brown, 3-4 mm long, sometimes green in the centre. Stamens six, pistil with three stigmas. Fruit dark brown, at least the tip. Leaves round, 1-2.5 mm broad, hollow with cross-walls, the lowest sheaths usually more or less red. **H:** 10-40 cm. **Hab:** Moist, open soil, water courses and mud in disused ditches, warm springs and their outlets. Rather common. **Sim:** Alpine Rush (358). Jointed Rush differs in the more inclined flower branches, thicker leaves and stems, and more red-coloured base. **Fl:** July. **I:** Laugasef. (Rush family).

Inflorescence (r. 0.6)

360 Toad Rush
Juncus bufonius

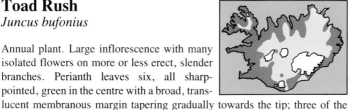

Annual plant. Large inflorescence with many isolated flowers on more or less erect, slender branches. Perianth leaves six, all sharp-pointed, green in the centre with a broad, trans-lucent membranous margin tapering gradually towards the tip; three of the outer leaves usually longer than the inner. Fruit light yellowish green or brown, shiny, shorter than the perianth. **H:** 5-20 cm. **Hab:** Moist, open soil, flushes, frequent colonizer of disturbed, moist habitats. Common. **Sim:** Frog Rush (361). The Toad Rush differs in being more upright, and in its more scattered inflorescence; the membranous margin of the inner perianth leaves tapers gradually to a sharp point. These two species have not always been treated separately, and are not clearly distinct. **Fl:** July-August. **I:** Lækjasef. (Rush family).

Fruit with perianth (m. 4)

361 Frog Rush
Juncus ranarius

Annual plant. The branches form dense, often prostrate rosettes. Most of the flowers single. Perianth leaves six; the outer three longer, sharply pointed, green in the centre with broad, transparent membranous margin which tapers gradually to a point; the inner three shorter, their membranous margin forming blunt tip surrounding the green central part, which is acute. Fruit light yellowish green or bright brown, shiny, shorter than the perianth. Leaves narrow (1 mm), linear. **H:** 2-10 cm. **Hab:** Moist, gravelly soil, open soil near springs, along streams or creeks, re-vegetating flushes. Rather common. **Sim:** Toad Rush (360). The Frog Rush differs in its prostrate growth, and the blunt membrane on the inner perianth leaves. **Fl:** July-August. **I:** Lindasef. (Rush family).

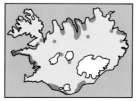

Fruit with perianth (m. 6)

362 Three-leaved Rush
Juncus trifidus

Slender culms in dense tufts, with numerous sheaths from previous year at the base. Flowers few (1-4) in small clusters. Perianth leaves six, dark brown, shiny, sharply pointed, with mem-branous margin above. Stamens six with light yellow anthers. Pistil light green; long style with trifid stigma. Leaves very slender (0.2-0.5 mm), chan-nelled. Bracts long, by far exceeding the inflorescence. **H:** 8-25 cm. **Hab:** Tussocks in dry heathland. Very common. **Sim:** None. **Fl:** June-July. **I:** Móasef. (Rush family).

Fruit with perianth (m. 7)

363 Chestnut Rush
Juncus castaneus

■☐
☐

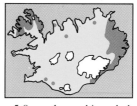

Rather coarse plant with one or two large, 5-10 flowered clusters, the upper smaller than the lower. Perianth leaves six, pointed, dark brown. Stamens six with yellowish green anthers. Short style with trifid stigma. Fruit large, 5-8 mm long, shiny, dark brown at the tip, clearly beaked. Leaves sturdy, channelled, 1-2.5 mm broad. **H:** 10-30 cm. **Hab:** Moist open soil, near creeks or seepage water. Rather rare. **Sim:** None. **Fl:** June-July. **I:** Dökkasef. (Rush family). — **Heath Rush** *Juncus squarrosus* is a very rare species resembling Chestnut Rush. Grows in dense tufts. Perianth leaves with broader membranous margin, inflorescence lighter; fruits smaller, leaves coarse and stiff. — **Saltmarsh Rush** *Juncus gerardi* is a very rare species of saltmarsh. It is tall, related to the Heath ?ush, with more delicate, numerous flower-clusters; the bract shorter than the inflorescence. Found only in one locality in the SW.

Fruit with perianth (m. 3)

364 Thread Rush
Juncus filiformis

☐■
☐

Culms round, rather slender, needle-shaped; flowers appearing densely clustered about the centre of stem or lower; in reality the bract of the inflorescence continues directly from the top of stem, often exceeding the stem length. Perianth 6-leaved, pointed, light brown or greenish. Stamens six with yellowish green anthers. Pistil red with pink, trifid stigma. Fruits shiny, light brown. Light brown sheath near base with short bristle instead of blade. **H:** 20-40 cm. **Hab:** Densely grown moist ground, moist creek banks and slopes. Common except in the South. **Sim:** Iceland Rush (365). The Thread Rush differs in the slender culms, lighter inflorescence and the bract of same length or longer than the culm. **Fl:** June-July. **I:** Þráðsef. (Rush family).

Fruit with perianth (m. 7)

365 Iceland Rush
Juncus arcticus ssp. *intermedius*

☐☐
■

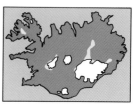

Culms round, needle-shaped, several flower-clusters in a rather dense inflorescence appearing lateral in upper part of culm. In reality it is the bract of the inflorescence that is needle-shaped, in direct continuation of the stem. Perianth 6-leaved. Perianth leaves pointed, dark brown. Six stamens with yellowish green anthers. Pistil red with short style and trifid, pink stigma, matures into a triangular, dark brown fruit. Culm rather thick, stiff, round, hollow, 1.5-2 mm wide. Leaves form sheaths on stem near base, without any blade. **H:** 25-45 cm. **Hab:** Damp banks, moist sandy river beds, margins where bogs and dry heathlands meet. Common. **Sim:** Thread Rush (364). The Iceland Rush differs in the stronger culms, darker inflorescence and the bract which is much shorter than the culm. **I:** Hrossanál. (Rush family).

Fruit with perianth (m. 5)

Protected plants

The following plants are protected by Icelandic law, wherever they are found growing wild. It is forbidden to tear off these plants any shoots, leaves, flowers or roots, to trample on them, dig them up or injure them in any other way.

Amphibious Bistort *Persicaria amphibia*
Arctic Poppy (a variety with white and pink flowers) *Papaver radicatum* ssp. *Stefanssonii*
Common Dog-violet, *Viola riviniana*
Common Twayblade *Listera ovata*
Eyebright, (a hot-spring variety) *Euphrasia calida*
Field Garlic *Allium oleraceum*
Foliolose Saxifrage *Saxifraga foliolosa*
Forked Spleenwort *Asplenium septentrionale*
Glaucous Dog-rose *Rosa dumalis*
Green Spleenwort *Asplenium viride*
Greenland Primrose *Primula egaliksensis*
Hard Fern (a variety restricted to hot springs) *Blechnum spicant* var. *fallax*
Heath-grass *Sieglingia decumbens*

Herb-paris *Paris quadrifolia*
Hudson Bay Sedge *Carex heleonastes*
Large Yellow-sedge, *Carex flava*
Lesser Spurrey *Spergularia salina*
Maidenhair Spleenwort *Asplenium trichomanes*
Marsh Bedstraw *Galium palustre*
Moonwort, Glossy *Botrychium simplex*
Northern Stichwort *Stellaria calycantha*
Parsley Fern *Cryptogramma crispa*
Pedunculate Water-starwort *Callitriche brutia*
Pigmyweed *Crassula aquatica*
Pyramidal Bugle *Ajuga pyramidalis*
Saltmarsh Rush *Juncus gerardi*
Stag's-horn Clubmoss *Lycopodium clavatum*
Tormentil *Potentilla erecta*
Wilson's Filmy-fern *Hymenophyllum wilsonii*
Wood-sorrel *Oxalis acetosella*

Index of families

Index to scientific names

Scientific names used in this book are printed in boldface in the index. The numbers are plant numbers, not page numbers. The letters A or B following a number refer to additional species described but not illustrated in the book. Abbreviated author names (omitted in the text) follow the species names according to the international rules of botanical nomenclature.

Index to Icelandic names

The species names recommended in this book are printed in boldface in the index. Other names commonly in use are printed in normal type. The numbers are plant numbers, not page numbers. The letters A or B following a number refer to additional species described but not illustrated. If the same name has been used elsewhere for more than one species, this is a indicated by a reference to the notes following the index.

301

*1 In *Íslenzkar jurtir* this name is used for the Glaucous Sedge.

*2 In *Íslenzkar jurtir* and *Íslenzk ferðaflóra* this name is used for the Roseroot.

*3 This name has in previous books been used for the Lesser Nettle (*Urtica urens*), but this is changed here in accordance with general Icelandic usage.

*4 In *Íslenzk ferðaflóra*, 2. ed. this name is mistakenly used for the Marsh Saxifrage (*Saxifraga hirculus*.

*5 In *Íslenzkar jurtir* and *Íslenzk ferðaflóra*, this name is used for a variety of Valerian.

*6 In *Íslenzk ferðaflóra* this name is used for the Slender Spikerush (*Eleocharis uniglumis*).

*7 This name has often been used for the Viviparous Fescue (*Festuca vivipara*), buit should instead be used for the Sheep's Fescue (*Festuca ovina*), which is not known to grow wild in Iceland.

*8 This name has generally been used for the Garden Lupin (*Lupinus polyphyllus*) rather than the Nootka Lupin (*Lupinus nootkatensis).

*9 In *Íslenzkar jurtir* this name is used for the Slender Spikerush (*Eleocharis uniglumis*).

*10 In *Íslenzk ferðaflóra* this name is used for the Common Spikerush (*Eleocharis palustris*).

Index to common names

Common names used in this book are printed in boldface in the index. The numbers are plant numbers, not page numbers. The letters A or B following a number refer to additional species described but not illustrated in the book.

Bibliography

Books for the identification of Icelandic plants

Bjarnason, Ágúst. *Íslenzk flóra*. Reykjavík: Iðunn, 1983.

Löve, Áskell. *Íslenzkar jurtir*. Copenhagen: Munksgård, 1945.

Löve, Áskell. *Íslenzk ferðaflóra*. Reykjavík: Almenna Bókafélagið, 1970. 2. ed. 1977.

Löve, Áskell. *Flora of Iceland*. (Translation of *Íslenzk ferðaflóra*). Reykjavík: Almenna bókafélagið, 1983.

Ostenfeld, C.H. and Gröntved, Johs. *The Flora of Iceland and the Faeroes*. Copenhagen & London, 1934.

Stefánsson, Stefán. *Flóra Íslands*. 1. ed. Copenhagen, 1901. 2. ed. Copenhagen, 1924. 3. ed. Reykjavík: The Icelandic Natural History Society, 1948.

Wolsley, Pat. *Flowering Plants of Iceland. Field Key*. Sandwick: Thuleprint, 1979.

Further references referred to in the introduction.

Dony, J.G., S.L. Jury and F.H. Perring. *English Names of Wild Flowers*. 2. ed. Reading: The Botanical Society of the British Isles, 1986.

Fitter, R. and A. Fitter. *The Wild Flowers of Britain and Northern Europe*. 3. ed. London: Collins 1978.

Hubbard, C.E. *Grasses*. 2. ed. Penguin Books, 1968.

Jermy, A.C. and T.G. Tutin. *British Sedges*. London: The Botanical Society of the British Isles, 1968.